STATISTICS,

TESTS and MEASUREMENTS

in PHYSICAL EDUCATION

STATISTICS,

TESTS and MEASUREMENTS

in PHYSICAL EDUCATION

By N. P. NEILSON, Ph.D.
**Department of
Health, Physical Education and
Recreation
University of Utah**

National Texts
Palo Alto, California

GV
436
.N42

Copyright © 1960
by
N. P. Neilson

National Texts
Published by N-P Publications, Palo Alto, California
Library of Congress Catalog Card Number 60-15233
Manufactured in the United States of America

Preface

Significant changes have taken place in the programs of physical education during recent years. Among these changes are the increase in facilities and time allotment, a more adequate preparation of teachers, and a more scientific approach to the solution of current problems. Progress to a considerable extent has been due to improvement of the devices used in measuring and testing the performance, achievement, and ability of our pupils.

To be adequately prepared, teachers of physical education should include in their professional preparation a basic course in physical education tests and measurements. Such a course requires an understanding of the concepts in educational statistics. In many instances the four-year course for majors in physical education becomes so heavy that students cannot find time for the course in statistics unless it is made a requirement. One important advantage of giving a combined course in statistics and tests and measurements is that majors find it especially helpful to work their problems in statistics using as data, for example, high jump and archery scores rather than reading scores, intelligence scores or similar data.

This book is not complete in itself, but is intended to serve as a guide for the instructor and class members in the intelligent use of the selected references and bibliography. Major concepts should be thoroughly emphasized, and the tests most useful in accomplishing objectives in a practical school situation should be studied in detail. It may be desirable to spend one-third of the allotted time to laboratory work. The suggested assignments may be modified from year to year.

While the book seems appropriate for use in any institution of higher learning, it should prove to be particularly helpful in state teachers' colleges, liberal arts colleges, private colleges, and small colleges.

N. P. Neilson

Table of Contents

		Page
SELECTED TEXTS AND REFERENCES		ix
I	ELEMENTARY STATISTICAL METHODS	1
	The Frequency Distribution	1
	Measures of Central Tendency	4
	Measures of Variability	10
	Reliability of Measures	15
	Correlation - Measures of Relationship	18
II	ELEMENTARY GRAPHICAL METHODS	24
	Frequency Polygon	24
	Histogram or Column Diagram	26
	Bar Diagram	27
	Ogive or Cumulative Frequency Graph	27
	Normal Probability Curve	27
	Skewness	28
III	DEVELOPMENT OF MEASUREMENT IN PHYSICAL EDUCATION (historical background)	30
IV	NEED FOR TESTS IN PHYSICAL EDUCATION	33
V	TERMINOLOGY AND CLASSIFICATION OF TESTS	36
	Definition of Terms	36
	Classification of Tests	39
VI	METHODS OF SCORING TESTS	41
	Sigma Index Scores	42
	Increased Increment Scale	43
VII	CRITERIA FOR EVALUATING AND SELECTING TESTS	44
	Criteria for Selecting Tests	44
	Sources of Unreliability in a Test	45
	Methods of Increasing Reliability	45
VIII	ANALYSIS OF SOME EXISTING TESTS	47
	Individual Oral Reports	47
	Class Abstracts	49
	Reports	53
IX	TEST CONSTRUCTION IN PHYSICAL EDUCATION	56
X	TEST ADMINISTRATION	58
GENERAL BIBLIOGRAPHY		59
APPENDIX		61

Selected Texts and References

1. American Physical Education Association. American Physical Education Review, 1895-1930.

2. American Association for Health, Physical Education, and Recreation.
   (a) Journal of Health, Physical Education, and Recreation, 1930-1960.
   (b) The Research Quarterly, 1930-1960.
   (c) Youth Fitness Test Manual, 1958. 64 pages

3. Bovard, John F.; Cozens, F. W.; Hagman, E. Patricia. Tests and Measurements in Physical Education, 3rd ed. Philadelphia: W. B. Saunders Company, 1949. 410 pages

4. Clarke, H. Harrison. Application of Measurement to Health and Physical Education, 3rd ed. Englewood Cliffs, N. J.: Prentice-Hall, Inc., 1959. 528 pages

5. Cureton, T. K. Physical Fitness Appraisal and Guidance. St. Louis: C. V. Mosby Company, 1947. 566 pages

6. Hunsicker, Paul A. and Montoye, Henry J. Applied Tests and Measurements in Physical Education. Englewood Cliffs, N. J.: Prentice-Hall, Inc., 1953. 149 pages

7. Larson, Leonard A. and Yocom, Rachael D. Measurement and Evaluation in Physical, Health, and Recreation Education. St. Louis: C. V. Mosby Company, 1951. 507 pages

8. Mathews, Donald K. Measurement in Physical Education. Philadelphia: W. B. Saunders Company, 1958. 359 pages

9. McCloy, Charles H. and Carpenter, Aileen. Laboratory Manual for Tests and Measurements in Health and Physical Education. New York: F. S. Crofts and Co., 1941. 140 pp.

10. McCloy, Charles H. and Young, Norma D. Tests and Measurements in Health and Physical Education, 3rd ed. New York: Appleton-Century-Crofts, Inc., 1954. 497 pages

11. Rogers, Frederick Rand. Physical Capacity Tests. New York: A. S. Barnes and Co., 1931. 54 pp. (now Ronald Press)

12. Weiss, Raymond A. and Phillips, Marjorie. Administration of Tests in Physical Education. St. Louis: C. V. Mosby Company, 1954. 278 pages

13. Willgoose, Carl E. Evaluation in Health Education and Physical Education. New York: McGraw-Hill Book Company, Inc., 1961, 478 pages

I. Elementary Statistical Methods

<u>References</u>. See Selected Texts and References No. 3, 4, and 10.

THE FREQUENCY DISTRIBUTION

How do you make a frequency distribution? Most measures can be arranged in a <u>continuous series</u>. A series theoretically capable of any degree of subdivision is defined as a continuous series. <u>Height</u> can be measured in feet, inches, and tenths of an inch. Series of measures which cannot be subdivided <u>without destroying the unit</u> are called "discrete" or "discontinuous" series. The number of <u>children</u> in a class and the number of <u>balls</u> in the storeroom are examples of <u>discrete series</u>.

The data appearing on the following page were taken from case cards 176 to 200, inclusive, of 2800 high school boys tested in four athletic events.

Our first method of interpreting a mass of measures is to arrange them in a frequency distribution. In order to tabulate the scores into a frequency distribution, we must: (1) determine the range; (2) decide upon the number and size of groups to be used in the classification; (3) tabulate separate measures within their proper step or group intervals.

The range is found by subtracting the lowest score from the highest. A class interval should be selected so that the total number of intervals will not be less than 10, not more than 20, and will be an odd number whenever possible. There are three methods of expressing the limits of a step interval; they are:

(a)	(b)	(c)
130 - 135	130 - 134.99	130 - 134
125 - 130	125 - 129.99	125 - 129
120 - 125	120 - 124.99	120 - 124

Either method (b) or (c) is preferable to (a). Best results are obtained by using method (b). Why?

In a frequency distribution we always assume that the scores within a given interval are spread evenly over the entire interval. If we wish to represent all of the scores within a given interval by some single value, the midpoint of the interval is the most logical choice.

DATA I. CRUDE SCORES -- (X) (Y) (Z)

Case	Age (months)	Height (inches)	Weight (pounds)	Bar Vault (inches)	High Jump (inches)	100-yd. Run (fifths of sec.)	Broad Jump (inches)
1	200	65	126	52	56	64	199
2	196	66	156	54	50	67	196
3	249	68	143	64	55	63	193
4	205	67	125	58	47	63	197
5	198	69	132	53	51	70	168
6	196	66	121	46	48	70	166
7	182	62	97	58	48	64	176
8	214	69	147	63	48	61	199
9	175	68	145	53	47	68	187
10	173	60	124	44	44	77	149
11	189	63	111	51	45	66	177
12	188	63	100	45	45	69	174
13	220	69	145	66	59	64	214
14	177	51	61	36	32	93	112
15	179	64	112	63	47	66	185
16	207	70	136	53	49	65	177
17	193	68	138	53	54	69	196
18	190	67	137	54	47	65	170
19	210	70	143	56	50	66	166
20	185	67	129	53	49	65	167
21	183	65	118	48	45	70	177
22	176	60	90	45	41	78	141
23	196	68	157	69	55	60	204
24	207	68	150	54	53	65	187
25	189	68	127	48	49	66	185

Range =

*Mean =

*Have pupils record correct means after completion of Assignment No. 2.

Illustration

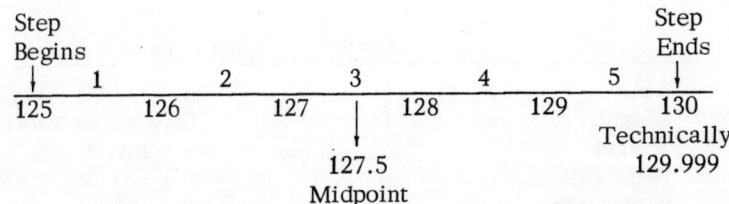

Midpoint = lower limit of step + $\dfrac{(\text{Upper limit} - \text{Lower limit})}{2}$

i.e., $127.5 = 125 + \dfrac{130 - 125}{2}$; also: $127.5 = \dfrac{125 + 130}{2}$

ILLUSTRATION OF A FREQUENCY DISTRIBUTION

DATA II

Scores: 18, 21, 22, 23, 20, 21, 25, 22, 17, 24, 20, 22, 19, 21, 25, 20, 21, 20, 22, 21, 23, 16, 19, 21, 24, 18, 20, 23, 16, 23, 22, 21, 22, 21, 19, 21, 22, 20, 20, 26, 19. 21, 22, 21, 18

	Scores (midpoints)	Tabulation	Frequency
High Score =	26	1	1
	25	11	2
	24	11	2
	23	1111	4
	22	1111 111	8
	21	1111 1111 1	11
	20	1111 11	7
	19	1111	4
	18	111	3
	17	1	1
Low Score =	16	11	2
			N = 45

ASSIGNMENT No. 1

(Note: All assignments are to be completed on $8\frac{1}{2} \times 11$" paper, folded lengthwise; name on outside. Keep problems in same order as they appear in the assignment.)

4   Statistics, Tests and Measurements in Physical Education

(a) Using Data I from page 2, make a frequency distribution for each factor under the following conditions:

For	Interval	Beginning of Top Step
Age	5	245 - 249.99
Height	1	70 (used as Midpoint)
Weight	5	155 - 159.99
Bar Vault	3	68 - 70.99
High Jump	2	58 - 59.99
100 Yards	3	92 - 94.99
Broad Jump	6	212 - 217.99

(b) State the range for each distribution.

(c) In the Bar Vault, what is the midpoint of the third step from the top?

(d) In the Broad Jump, what is the midpoint of the second step from the top?

(e) N = the number of cases. What does N equal for Weight? For High Jump?

MEASURES OF CENTRAL TENDENCY

Measures of Central Tendency are points on a scale. They give us a single measure which best represents the whole group; they give us a chance to compare two groups. The three measures of central tendency are: (1) the Mean or Average; (2) the Median; (3) the Mode.

The Mean. The Mean (Average) is the best known and most used measure of central tendency. Let M = Mean; Σ = Sum of; X = Score; N = Number of Cases; F = Frequency; $\overline{M}$ = Midpoint of each step.

(a) When the scores are ungrouped, and using scores as midpoints: $M = \dfrac{\Sigma X}{N}$

Example

$\overline{X}$
8
6
2
9
4
3
3
$\Sigma X = \overline{35}$

$N = 7$

$M = \dfrac{35}{7}$

$M = 5$

(b) When the scores are grouped: $M = \dfrac{\Sigma(F \times \overline{M})}{N}$

Example

Steps	Midpoint ($\overline{M}$)	F	(F × $\overline{M}$)
45 - 49.99	47.5	1	47.5
40 - 44.99	42.5	3	127.5
35 - 39.99	37.5	5	187.5
30 - 34.99	32.5	4	130.0
25 - 29.99	27.5	2	55.0
20 - 24.99	22.5	1	22.5
		N = 16	Σ = 570.0

$M = \dfrac{570}{16}$

$M = 35.62$

(c) When the scores are grouped (Guessed Average Method):

1. Organize the data in a frequency distribution.

2. Guess an average near the center of the distribution. The G.A. should be at the <u>midpoint</u> of the step interval.

3. Find the deviation "d" in terms of step intervals, of the midpoint of each step from the G.A.

4. Multiply the "d" of each step by its corresponding frequency "f".

5. Find the algebraic sum of the plus and minus "fd's" and divide this sum by the number of cases "N". This obtained result is called "c" (the correction in obtaining the G.A. in terms of step intervals).

6. Multiply "c" by the size of the step interval to obtain "C" (the correction in terms of the scores).

7. Add "C" algebraically to the G.A. to get the Mean.

Example:

Scores	f	d	fd	
90 - 99.9	3	5	15	Mean = G.A. + C
80 - 89.9	8	4	32	C = c × S.I.
70 - 79.9	12	3	36	$c = \frac{\Sigma fd}{N}$
60 - 69.9	15	2	30	f = frequency
50 - 59.9	20	1	20 (+133)	d = deviation
(G.A.) 40 - 49.9	20	0		G.A. = 45
30 - 39.9	15	-1	-15	58 = algebraic sum of plus and minus fd's
20 - 29.9	12	-2	-24	116 = no. of cases
10 - 19.9	8	-3	-24	10 = size of step interval
0 - 9.9	3	-4	-12 (-75)	
	N = 116		Σfd = 58	

Mean   G.A. + ($\frac{\Sigma fd}{N}$ × size of interval)

Mean   45 + ($\frac{58}{116}$ times 10)

Mean   45 + .5 × 10 = 50

NOTE: Guessed Average, Assumed Mean, and Arbitrary Origin mean the same thing; hence use of the abbreviations G.A., A.M., and A.O.

ASSIGNMENT No. 2

(a) Using Data I, compute the mean for each of the seven factors, using the formula:

$$M = \frac{\Sigma X}{N}$$

(b) Using Data I, and the groupings suggested under Assignment No. 1, compute the mean for Height and for High Jump. Use the formula:

$$M = \frac{\Sigma (F \times \bar{M})}{N}$$

Elementary Statistical Methods   7

(c) Using Data I, and the groupings suggested under Assignment No. 1, compute the mean for Height; for 100 Yards. Use the Guessed Average method.

The Median. The median is that point on a scale above which and below which 50% of the cases lie. It may be found by counting off one-half of the measures, i.e., $\frac{N}{2}$ from either end of the series.

Continuous Series

CASE 1   (N is odd; N = 11; $\frac{N}{2}$ = 5.5)

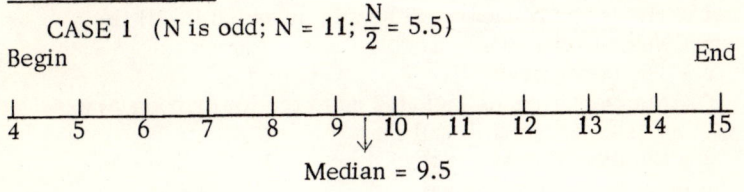

Median = 9.5

CASE 2   (N is even; N = 10; $\frac{N}{2}$ = 5)

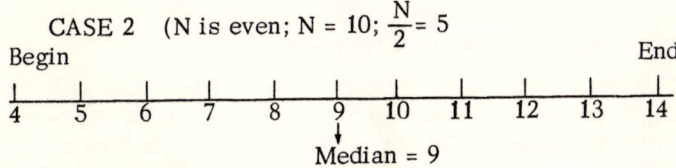

Median = 9

Discrete Series

CASE 1   (N is odd; N = 11; $\frac{N+1}{2}$ = 6)

There is now no value that defines the Median as the midpoint in the series. The middle measure can be found by counting $\frac{N+1}{2}$ or 6 scores from either end of the series. Beginning with 4, the midscore = 9. If 11 balls were used, it would be the sixth ball.

CASE 2   (N is even; N = 10; $\frac{N+1}{2}$ = 5.5)

Here there is no median value and no midscore. In cases like this it is customary to take the midscore arbitrarily at a point midway between the middlemost scores.
$\frac{N+1}{2}$ = 5.5. If 10 balls were used, it would be between the fifth and sixth balls.

Grouped Data

In grouped data the frequencies in each interval must be considered as evenly distributed between the interval limits, no matter how few cases the frequency represents. The median being the 50 percentile, we can use the "Any Percentile formula" to find the median.

Any Percentile Formula $\qquad P = i + \dfrac{np - n'}{f} \times (v)$

P = Any percentile to be found
i = The lower boundary of the step in which P will lie
n = Number of cases
p = The percentage
n' = Number of cases included up to the lower boundary of step in which P will lie
f = Number of cases in that step
v = Value of step interval

Example. Find the median or 50 percentile.

To find the step in which the median or 50 percentile will lie, multiply the number of cases in the distribution by the percentile and then add that number of cases from the bottom of the distribution. Draw lines above and below the step in which the number falls.

Steps	f		Computation
30 - 32	2		$P = i + \dfrac{np - n'}{f} (v)$
27 - 29	3	(5)	
24 - 26	8	(13)	
21 - 23	11		$N(34) \times p(.50) = 17$ cases
			The 17th case will lie in
18 - 20.9	6	(10)	step 21 - 23
15 - 17.99	4		Median $= i + \dfrac{(34)(.50) - n'}{f} \times (3)$
	N = 34		

$$Md = 21 + \dfrac{17 - 10}{11} \times (3) = 21 + 1.91$$

$$Md = 22.91$$

In a similar manner the 10th, 20th, 24th, or any percentile can be found.

The Mode. The mode is that measure at which most frequencies fall. When scores are grouped, the midpoint of the step having the greatest frequency is taken as the Mode. Distributions may be unimodal (one mode), bimodal (two modes), or polymodal (with more than two modes). The Mode is the least reliable, but easiest to compute, measure of central tendency.

When To Use the Mean, Median, and Mode

Use the Mean:

1. When each score should have equal weight in determining the central tendency.
2. When the highest reliability is desired.
3. When correlations or measures of reliability are to be computed.

Use the Median:

1. When an easily computed measure of central tendency is desired.
2. When there are extreme measures that would distort the average.

Use the Mode:

1. When an approximate measure of concentration is desired.
2. When the most frequently recurring score is sought.

If the data are "normal" the mean, median, and mode will be the same.

ASSIGNMENT No. 3

(a) Using Data I and the groupings suggested under Assignment No. 1, compute the median for Height, and Broad Jump. (Use the Any Percentile formula.)

(b) Using Data I, and the groupings suggested under Assignment No. 1, list the mode or modes for each of the seven factors.

(c) Using Data I, and the groupings suggested under Assignment No. 1, find the 60 percentile for High Jump; find the 20 percentile for Weight.

10   Statistics, Tests and Measurements in Physical Education

MEASURES OF VARIABILITY

Measures of variability are measures of spread or scatter and are distances on a scale in contrast to points on a scale. Two distributions may have the same mean, but one distribution may be more variable than the other. Four measures of variability are: (1) range, (2) quartile deviation or Q, (3) average deviation or AD, and (4) standard deviation or SD or σ.

1. The Range. The range is the most general (least reliable) measure of spread or scatter, and includes 100% of the cases in the distribution. The range may be expressed in two ways: (a) 24 to 68, (b) 44, which is 68 - 24. It is used only when one wishes to make a rough comparison of two groups for variability.

2. The Quartile Deviation or Q or Semi-Interquartile Range. Q is defined as one-half the distance from the 25 percentile to the 75 percentile. Let Q_1 = the 25 percentile; Q_3 = the 75 percentile.

   $Q = \dfrac{Q_3 - Q_1}{2}$ It will be remembered that Q_2 = the 50 percentile or the median. The Any Percentile formula may be used to find Q_3 and Q_1, the values then substituted in the formula, and Q found.

   Example. Assume 16 cases:

   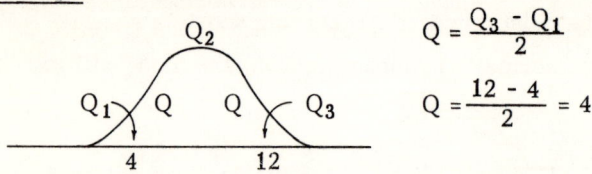

   $Q = \dfrac{Q_3 - Q_1}{2}$

   $Q = \dfrac{12 - 4}{2} = 4$

   One Q on each side of the median (also the mean in a normal distribution) marks off the limits within which fall the middle 50% of the measures in the distribution. If the scores are scattered, the quartiles will be relatively far apart and Q will be large. In a normal curve, the quartile deviation will be the same as the probable error, since each theoretically includes 50% of the cases. The quartile deviation is used with the median, and the probable error with the mean.

3. The Average Deviation or AD. The AD is defined as the average of the deviations of all the separate scores in a series

taken from their central tendency (mean, median, or mode). The AD is generally computed from the mean. In averaging deviations, no account is taken of signs. Suppose we have seven scores: 9, 10, 13, 16, 18, 19, 20. The mean is, then, 15. To find the deviation of each measure, we subtract the mean from it. The deviations would be:

$$D = X - M$$

X	M	D
9 - 15 =		-6
10 - 15 =		-5
13 - 15 =		-2
16 - 15 =		+1
18 - 15 =		+3
19 - 15 =		+4
20 - 15 =		+5

Adding without regard to signs, Σ of Deviations = 26

The formula for the AD with ungrouped numbers is:

$$AD = \frac{\Sigma D}{N} \qquad N = 7 \qquad \Sigma D = 26$$

substituting: $\frac{26}{7} = 3.71 = AD$

When the data are grouped, we find the deviation of the midpoint of each step from the average. When more than one case falls at a step the D is multiplied by the frequency, so we have FD. The formula for AD for measures grouped in a frequency distribution is:

$$AD = \frac{\Sigma (F \times D)}{N}$$

In a normal distribution the AD, when measured off above and below the mean, marks the limits of the middle 57.5% of the measures or cases. The AD is, therefore, slightly larger than Q.

4. The Standard Deviation or SD or σ. The standard deviation is the most reliable of the measures of variability and hence is used most in research that requires great accuracy.

σ is the square root of the arithmetic mean of the squared deviations taken from the average of the distribution. In a normal distribution when measured off above and below the mean, σ marks the limits of the middle 68.26% (roughly two-thirds) of the distribution.

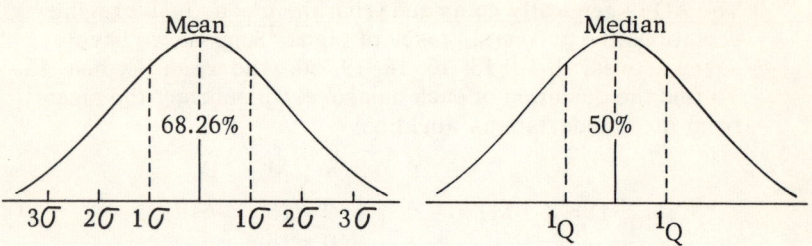

Differences between AD and σ:

1. In AD we disregard signs when adding deviations.
2. In σ we avoid differences in signs by squaring.
3. Deviations for σ are always taken from the mean.
4. Deviations for AD can be taken from the mean, median, or mode.

The formula for the σ of a series of ungrouped numbers is:

$$\sigma = \sqrt{\frac{\Sigma D^2}{N}}$$

The Crude Score formula is derived from this and is:

$$\sigma = \sqrt{\frac{\Sigma X^2}{N} - M_x^2} \qquad \text{because } D = X - M$$

The mean found by adding the crude scores and dividing by N should be used in the crude score formula.

<u>Example.</u> Using $\sigma = \sqrt{\frac{\Sigma D^2}{N}}$

X	M	D	D²
7	4	3	9
6	4	2	4
5	4	1	1
4	4	0	0
3	4	-1	1
2	4	-2	4
1	4	-3	9

$\Sigma X = 28 \qquad \Sigma D^2 = 28$

$N = 7$

$M = \frac{\Sigma X}{N}$

$M = \frac{28}{7} = 4$

$D = X - M$

$\sigma = \sqrt{\frac{28}{7}}$

$\sigma = \sqrt{4} \; ; \; \sigma = 2$

Example. $\sigma = \sqrt{\dfrac{\Sigma X^2}{N} - M_x^2}$

X	X²
7	49
6	36
5	25
4	16
3	9
2	4
1	1

$\Sigma X = 28$ $\Sigma X^2 = 140$

$N = 7$ $\Sigma X = 28$

$M_x = \dfrac{\Sigma X}{N} = \dfrac{28}{7} = 4$

$M_x^2 = 16$

$\sigma = \sqrt{\dfrac{140}{7} - 16} = \sqrt{20 - 16}$

$\sigma = \sqrt{4} = 2$

When data are grouped $\sigma = \sqrt{\dfrac{\Sigma FD^2}{N}}$. The formula for the Guessed Average Method (a short method) is

$$\sigma = V\sqrt{\dfrac{\Sigma fd^2}{N} - c^2}$$

where V = the value of the step and $c = \dfrac{\Sigma fd}{N}$

Hence $\sigma = \sqrt{\dfrac{\Sigma fd^2}{N} - \left(\dfrac{\Sigma fd}{N}\right)^2}$ times the size of the interval. See Bovard, Cozens and Hagman, 3rd edition, page 270.

The Probable Error or P.E. When the frequency distribution curve is normal, the P.E. may be used as a measure of variability and is defined as .6745 σ. Plus and minus one P.E. includes 50% of the cases. The P.E. of a distribution equals .6745 times the σ of the distribution. In a normal distribution, the P.E. therefore equals Q.

On the following page is an example showing the extraction of the square root.

To Extract the Square Root

```
            6    9.67
         √ 48' 54.60
       6√   36
            ────
     129   1254
           1161
           ────
    1386   9360
           8316
           ─────
   13927   104400
            97489
            ─────
             6911
```

Example. Let the number equal 4854.6. Begin at the decimal point, mark off two places at a time to the left and to the right; estimate the root of the first number; place the root as the divisor and in the answer; multiply; subtract the result; bring down the next two figures; multiply your answer obtained thus far by 2 and add a zero for another digit place (120, this is the new divisor); replace the zero in the divisor by the next root to appear in the answer and multiply again; continue the procedure.

When To Use the Range, Quartile Deviation, A.D., and σ

Use the Range:
1. When the data are too scant to justify the calculation of any other measure of variability.
2. When a knowledge of the total spread is all that is necessary.

Use the Quartile Deviation (Q):
1. For a quick measure of variability.
2. When there are extreme measures.
3. When the median is used as the measure of central tendency.

Use the Average Deviation:
1. When it is desired to weight all deviations according to their size.
2. When extreme deviations should not influence the measure of variability.

Use the Standard Deviation:
1. When the highest reliability is sought.
2. When extreme deviations are desired, to influence the measure of variability.
3. When correlations or measures of reliability are to be computed later.

The Probable Error is a better measure of <u>reliability</u> than <u>variability</u>.

Elementary Statistical Methods

ASSIGNMENT No. 4

(a) Using Data I, and the groupings suggested under Assignment No. 1, find Q for Weight; for Bar Vault.

(b) Using Data I, and the (crude score) mean found under Assignment No. 2 (a), find the A.D. for Height. Use the formula:
$$AD = \frac{\Sigma D}{N}.$$

(c) Using Data I, the grouping suggested under Assignment No. 1, and the means found under Assignment No. 2 (b), find the A.D. for Height; for High Jump. Use the formula:
$$AD = \frac{\Sigma (F \times D)}{N}.$$

(d) Using the Crude Score formula, find the σ for each of the seven factors. The ΣX^2 may be found on page 16, and the computed means on page 2.

(e) Using the formula, Guessed Average Method,

$$\sigma = \sqrt{\frac{\Sigma fd^2}{N} - \left(\frac{\Sigma fd}{N}\right)^2}$$ (times the size of the step)

and the grouping suggested under Assignment No. 1, find the σ for High Jump.

(f) Using σ found in (e) above, what is the P.E. of the distribution for High Jump?

RELIABILITY OF MEASURES

The reliability of a test is the amount of agreement between the results secured from two or more applications of the test to the same pupils by the <u>same examiner</u>.

Reliability is not the same as:

1. Accuracy of measurement or computations.

2. Validity. (A test measures what it is supposed to measure.)

3. Representativeness. (Example: The trait measured includes both sexes, all ages, all races, urban and rural.)

Reliability is an application of the theory of chance. <u>Increasing the number of cases increases the reliability</u>. Errors that

DATA III. (SQUARES FOR DATA I)

Case	Age	Height	Weight	Bar Vault	High Jump	100-yd. Run	Broad Jump
1	40000	4225	15876	2704	3136	4096	39601
2	38416	4356	24336	2916	2500	4489	38416
3	62001	4624	20449	4096	3025	3969	37249
4	42025	4489	15625	3364	2209	3969	38809
5	39204	4761	17424	2809	2601	4900	28224
6	38416	4356	14641	2116	2304	4900	27556
7	33124	3844	9409	3364	2304	4096	30976
8	45796	4761	21609	3969	2304	3721	39601
9	30625	4624	21025	2809	2209	4624	34969
10	29929	3600	15376	1936	1936	5929	22201
11	35721	3969	12321	2601	2025	4356	31329
12	35344	3969	10000	2025	2025	4761	30276
13	48400	4761	21025	4356	3481	4096	45796
14	31329	2601	3721	1296	1024	8649	12544
15	32041	4096	12544	3969	2209	4356	34225
16	42849	4900	18496	2809	2401	4225	31329
17	37249	4624	19044	2809	2916	4761	38416
18	36100	4489	18769	2916	2209	4225	28900
19	44100	4900	20449	3136	2500	4356	27556
20	34225	4489	16641	2809	2401	4225	27889
21	33489	4225	13924	2304	2025	4900	31329
22	30976	3600	8100	2025	1681	6084	19881
23	38416	4624	24649	4761	3025	3600	41616
24	42849	4624	22500	2916	2809	4225	34969
25	35721	4624	16129	2304	2401	4356	34225
ΣX^2	958345	108135	414081	73119	59660	115868	807882

*Sigma =

* Have pupils record correct sigmas after completion of Assignment No. 4.

Elementary Statistical Methods   17

arise from failure to get a random sample are neither detected nor measured by reliability formulas.

Objective data obtained in distributions are but samples of an infinite number of distributions that might be obtained if time permitted. The obtained mean of a distribution is the mean of a sampling and not the true mean. The σ of the mean $= \frac{\sigma \text{ of Dist.}}{\sqrt{N}}$. In 68.26% of the cases the true mean will lie between plus and minus 1 σ_M. The larger the number of cases, therefore, the nearer will be the mean to the true mean. Illustrate with a distribution of 100 means in the high jump.

The P.E. of the mean = σ_M times .6745; or, stated another way, .6745 σ_M.

$$PE_M = .6745 \left(\frac{\sigma \text{ (dist)}}{\sqrt{N}} \right)$$ What does this mean?

How nearly accurate is the σ of a distribution? If the distribution is approximately normal the $\sigma_\sigma = \frac{\sigma \text{ (dist)}}{\sqrt{2N}}$. In 68.26% of the cases the true σ of the distribution will lie between plus and minus one σ from the obtained σ of the distribution.

The reliability of the difference between two means may be found by the formula:

$$\sigma \text{ dif.} = \sqrt{\sigma_{M_1}^2 + \sigma_{M_2}^2}$$ Remember the

σ (Aver.) = $\frac{\sigma \text{ (dist.)}}{\sqrt{N}}$.

Then $\sigma_{\text{dif.}} = \sqrt{\left(\frac{\sigma \text{ dist.}}{\sqrt{N}} \right)_1^2 + \left(\frac{\sigma \text{ dist.}}{\sqrt{N}} \right)_2^2}$

In a normal distribution 9973 cases out of 10,000 will lie within plus and minus 3 σ on each side of the mean. When the difference divided by the σ of the difference $\left(\frac{\text{dif.}}{\sigma \text{ dif.}} \right)$ is greater than 3, we can be sure that a difference of the same sign as the obtained difference actually exists.

ASSIGNMENT No. 5

(a) Using the means and sigmas obtained by the crude score method, find the σ_M for each of the seven factors in Data I. (Carry out to three decimal places.)

(b) Find the $P.E._M$ for each of the seven factors, using the sigmas obtained by the crude score method.

(c) Find the σ_σ for each of the seven factors, using the sigmas obtained by the crude score method.

(d) When $M_1 = 7.80$; $\sigma_1 = 5.20$; $M_2 = 7.46$; $\sigma_2 = .68$; $N_1 = 49$; $N_2 = 36$; find the difference between the means. What is the σ of this difference?

CORRELATION (MEASURES OF RELATIONSHIP)

The statistical device whereby relationship is expressed on a quantitative scale is called the "Coefficient of Correlation," and is designated by the letter "r". The relation of the diameter to the circumference of a circle is perfect, or $r = 1$. If we change the diameter, we change the circumference by 3.1416 times that amount. Correlation expresses relationship. Numbers multiplied by themselves give a higher relationship than by any other combination.

Example
$1 \times 1 = 1$ $1 \times 2 = 2$
$2 \times 2 = 4$ $1 \times 3 = 3$
$3 \times 3 = \underline{9}$ $2 \times 3 = \underline{6}$
   14 11

The "r" can range from 0 to +1 or from 0 to -1 and, therefore, from -1 to +1. Remember that if "r" is greater than 1, the computation is incorrect. A positive correlation indicates positive relationship. A zero correlation indicates absence of relationship. A negative correlation indicates inverse relationship.

Elementary Statistical Methods 19

Example	r = -1		Example	r = +1	
Case	Factor X	Factor Y	Case	Factor X	Factor Y
a	1	5	a	1	1
b	2	4	b	2	2
c	3	3	c	3	3
d	4	2	d	4	4
e	5	1	e	5	5

The Crude Score formula for "r" is:

$$r = \frac{\frac{\Sigma XY}{N} - M_x M_y}{\sqrt{\frac{\Sigma X^2}{N} - M_x^2} \sqrt{\frac{\Sigma Y^2}{N} - M_y^2}}$$

This formula is derived from the Pearson Product-Moment formula where deviations are taken from the actual means of the two distributions:

$$r = \frac{\Sigma xy}{N \sigma_x \sigma_y}$$

When deviations are taken from guessed averages (assumed means), corrections are necessary and the corrections c_x and c_y

$$r = \frac{\frac{\Sigma xy}{N} - c_x c_y}{\sigma_x \sigma_y}$$

and the σ_x and σ_y have been left in units of step intervals to reduce the computation involved. There are other formulae for "r"; one by Rietz and one by Thorndyke.

Interpretation of "r"

The coefficient of correlation should be interpreted in relation to the character and extent of the problem under investigation. In one instance an "r" of .50 might be considered quite high, while in another instance an "r" of .50 might be considered too low to have much significance. A correlation of .80 is relatively substantial, and below .40 it is rather low or negligible.

COMBINATIONS OF FACTORS IN DATA I
(Code for the X times Y) $\frac{N(N-1)}{2}$

	X	Y		X	Y
1	Age	× Height	12	Weight	× Bar Vault
2	Age	× Weight	13	Weight	× High Jump
3	Age	× Bar Vault	14	Weight	× 100-yard
4	Age	× High Jump	15	Weight	× Broad Jump
5	Age	× 100-yard	16	Bar Vault	× High Jump
6	Age	× Broad Jump	17	Bar Vault	× 100-yard
7	Height	× Weight	18	Bar Vault	× Broad Jump
8	Height	× Bar Vault	19	High Jump	× 100-yard
9	Height	× High Jump	20	High Jump	× Broad Jump
10	Height	× 100-yard	21	100-yard	× Broad Jump
11	Height	× Broad Jump			

$$\frac{7(7-1)}{2} = 21$$

ASSIGNMENT No. 6

(a) Using the Crude Score means and sigmas already obtained, and using the Crude Score formula, compute the correlation for Height-Weight; Height-High Jump; Bar Vault-High Jump; and 100 yard-Broad Jump.

(b) Using the Crude Score formula, find "r" when X and Y scores are as follows (show computations):

X	Y	X^2	Y^2	XY
65	56			
66	51			
68	55			
67	47			
69	54			
66	48			
62	49			
69	52			
68	47			
60	46			
Σ =				

$$r = \frac{\frac{\Sigma XY}{N} - M_x M_y}{\sqrt{\frac{\Sigma X^2}{N} - M_x^2} \sqrt{\frac{\Sigma Y^2}{N} - M_y^2}}$$

Probable Error of an "r"

The probable error of an "r" is found by the formula:

$$PE_r = \frac{.6745 (1 - r^2)}{\sqrt{N}}$$. What does this mean?

The probable error of the difference between the two "r's" is:

$$PE_{(dif. \ r_1 - r_2)} = \sqrt{PE_{r_1}^2 + PE_{r_2}^2}$$

A difference is considered reliable when $\frac{Dif.}{PE_{(dif.)}}$ is 4 or more.

Regression

The prediction of success in one ability from performance in another is a problem of regression and regression lines. When two sets of scores are plotted in a form having OX and OY lines proportional to the σ's, and the lines are drawn connecting the means of the rows and the means of the columns, these lines are known as "relation lines." The best fitted lines drawn to the relation lines are the regression lines. Since the σ's represent equal distances on the two axes, respectively, the slopes of the two regression lines will be the correlation between the two abilities. The X-on-Y ratio = $\frac{x}{y}$ and the Y-on-X ratio = $\frac{y}{x}$. The regression lines have equations. In testing the reliability of predictions made from regression equations, the Standard Error of Estimate $\sigma_{(est.)}$ is used. (See Bovard, Cozens, Hagman, pages 281-285.)

Correlation Ratio or Eta or η

When the regression lines are not linear, but curvilinear, η should be used. η = r when the relation is linear; it will be greater than "r" when the relation is non-linear.

Partial Correlation

Partial correlation represents the net relationship existing between two variables when other variables which may affect the true relationship have been held constant. (See Bovard, Cozens, Hagman, pages 285-294.)

DATA IV. (XY FOR DATA I)

Case	2 Age Weight	7 Height Weight	9 Height High Jump	13 Weight High Jump	16 Bar Vault High Jump	20 High Jump Broad Jump	21 100-yard Broad Jump
1	25200	8190	3640	7056	2912	11144	12736
2	30576	10296	3300	7800	2700	9800	13132
3	35607	9724	3740	7865	3520	10615	12159
4	25625	8375	3149	5875	2726	9259	12411
5	26136	9108	3519	6732	2703	8568	11760
6	23716	7986	3168	5808	2208	7968	11620
7	17654	6014	2976	4656	2784	8448	11264
8	31458	10143	3312	7056	3024	9552	12139
9	25375	9860	3196	6815	2491	8789	12716
10	21452	7440	2640	5456	1936	6556	11473
11	20979	6993	2835	4995	2295	7965	11682
12	18800	6300	2835	4500	2025	7830	12006
13	31900	10005	4071	8555	3894	12626	13696
14	10797	3111	1632	1952	1152	3584	10416
15	20048	7168	3008	5264	2961	8695	12210
16	28152	9520	3430	6664	2597	8673	11505
17	26634	9384	3672	7452	2862	10584	13524
18	26030	9179	3149	6439	2538	7990	11050
19	30030	10010	3500	7150	2800	8300	10956
20	23865	8643	3283	6321	2597	8183	10855
21	21594	7670	2925	5310	2160	7965	12390
22	15840	5400	2460	3690	1845	5781	10998
23	30772	10676	3740	8635	3795	11220	12240
24	31050	10200	3604	7950	2862	9911	12155
25	24003	8636	3332	6223	2352	9065	12210
Σ XY	623,293	210,031	80,116	156,219	65,739	219,071	299,303

ASSIGNMENT No. 7

(a) Find the P.E. for each of the correlations found in Assignment No. 6 (a).

(b) Find the $PE_{(dif.)}$ between "r" found for Height-High Jump and the "r" found for Assignment No. 6 (b). Is the difference reliable?

(c) Following the example found on page 25, make an appropriate chart and compute the Product-Moment coefficient of correlation between Height and Broad Jump, using Data I. Find the PE_r.

II. Elementary Graphical Methods

Reference. Bovard, Cozens, Hagman: pages 296-308.

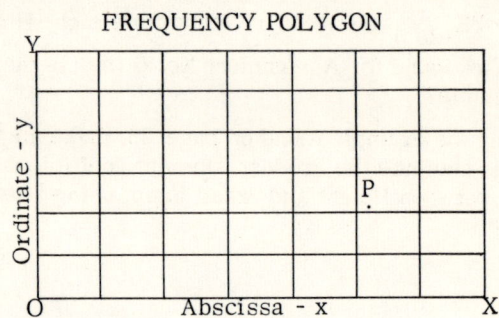

FREQUENCY POLYGON

Graphing or plotting is done in reference to two lines or "axes," the one vertical and the other horizontal.
   O = Origin
   OY = Ordinate or Y axis
   OX = Abscissa or X axis

Locate point P when X = 5 and Y = 2.

In a frequency polygon the frequency of any given interval is represented by its midpoint. In the frequency polygon, the area between the boundary line of the polygon and the base line represents the total frequency (N) of the distribution.

Frequency Polygon for High Jump (DATA I)

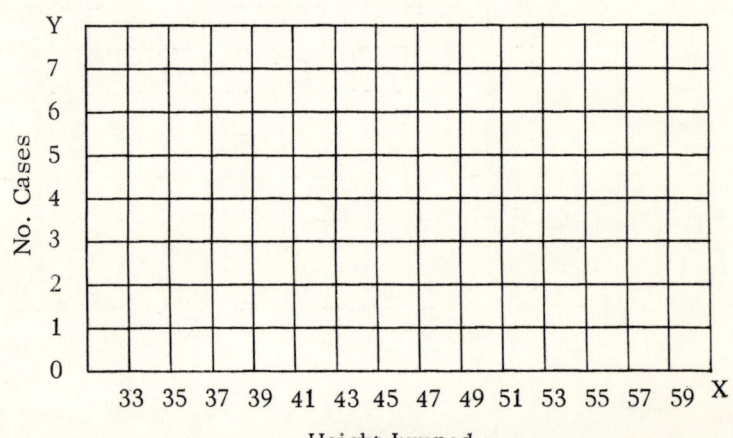

Elementary Graphical Methods

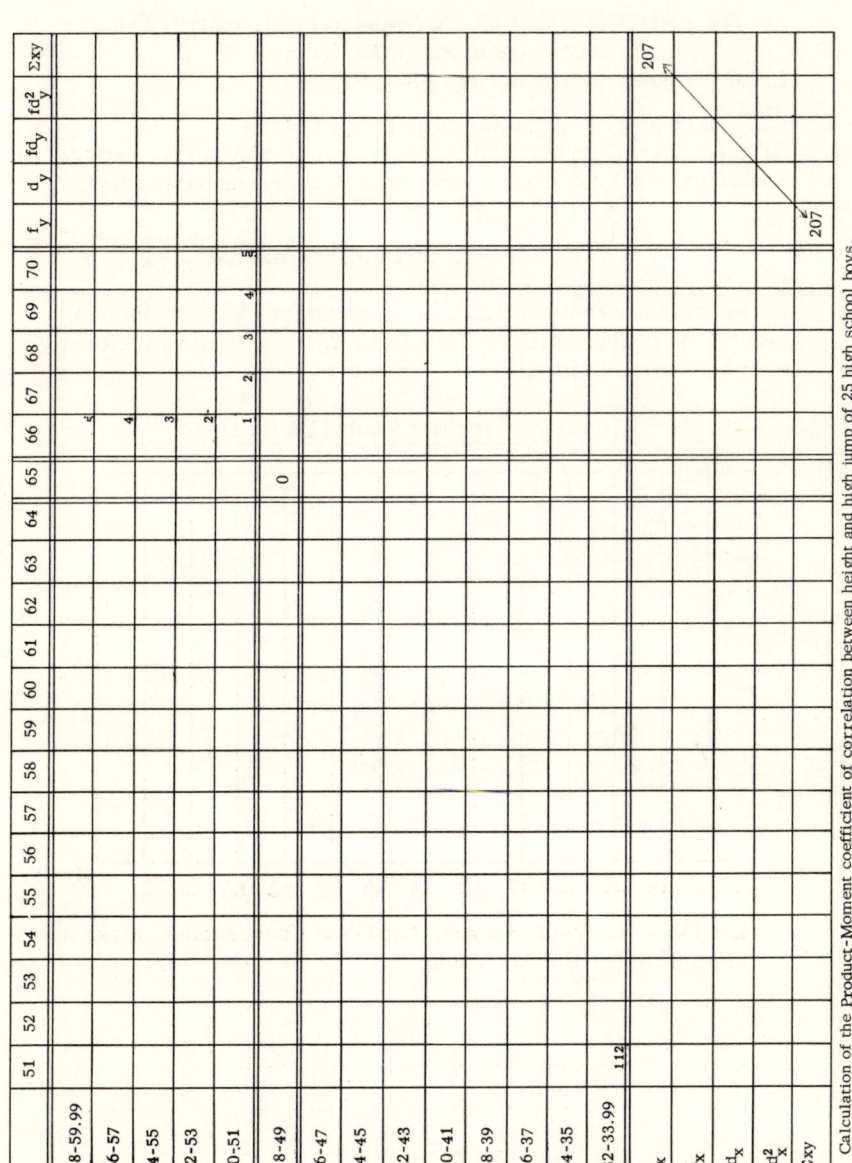

Calculation of the Product-Moment coefficient of correlation between height and high jump of 25 high school boys.

r = _____ ; PE_r = _____ .

Let OX = High Jump scores represented by midpoints of intervals under conditions in Assignment No. 1.
Let OY = Frequencies in High Jump, Data I.

Plot a frequency polygon for High Jump, Data I.
Graphs, charts, tables, and diagrams are useful in translating numerical facts into more concrete and understandable form.

HISTOGRAM OR COLUMN DIAGRAM

In the histogram the scores of a given interval are not considered as concentrated at the midpoint, but as spread uniformly over the entire interval.

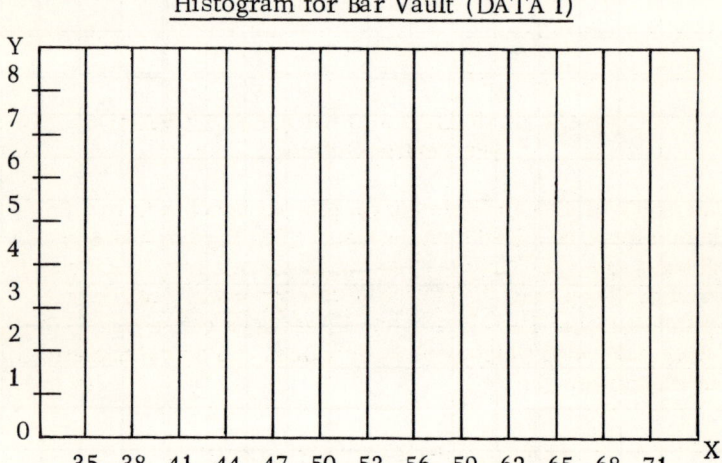

Histogram for Bar Vault (DATA I)

Let OX = Bar Vault Scores. Let OY = Frequencies. Make a histogram for the Bar Vault.

BAR DIAGRAM

Differences having one dimension can be shown adequately by a bar diagram. Below is a bar diagram showing the number of different marks given to a class.

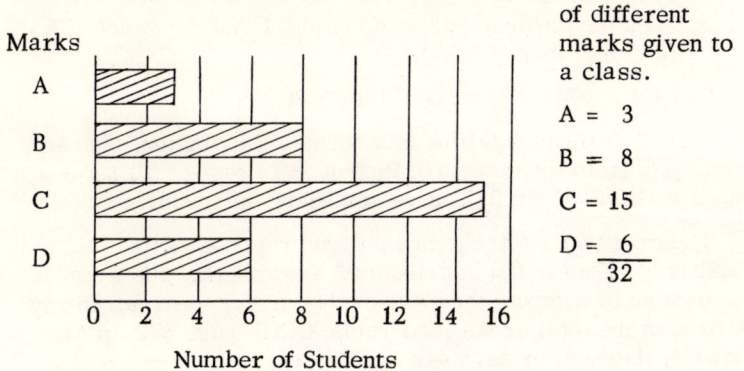

Marks

A = 3
B = 8
C = 15
D = 6
  ──
  32

(bar diagram: Number of Students, x-axis 0 to 16; A≈3, B≈8, C≈15, D≈6)

OGIVE OR CUMULATIVE FREQUENCY GRAPH
(Percentile Graph)

In order to plot an ogive curve, the frequencies in the distribution must be added cumulatively. (See Bovard, Cozens, Hagman, page 301.) In constructing an ogive curve, each cumulative frequency must be plotted at the upper limit of the step on which it falls. The chief value of the ogive curve lies in the relative ease with which percentile values can be calculated from the curve.

NORMAL PROBABILITY CURVE
(Normal Curve; Normal Frequency Curve)

The probability of an event is best stated as a ratio. This ratio always falls between the limits 0 and 1.00. If a coin is tossed once, the probability of its falling head is 1/2 and tail 1/2. If we toss two coins at the same time, the ratios are: 2 heads 1/4, one head and one tail 1/2, 2 tails 1/4. If we toss 20 pennies 100 times and plot the results, it will approximate a normal curve. The chances that the pennies would all fall heads or all fall tails would be very rare. In the normal curve, the mean, median, and mode fall at the same point and are therefore equal.

Between the mean and plus and minus 1σ the middle 68.26% of the cases are found.
Between the mean and plus and minus 1 PE the middle 50% of the cases are found.
Between the mean and plus and minus 1 AD the middle 57.5% of the cases are found.

One PE = .6745 σ ; 1σ = 1.4825 PE

With 10,000 cases falling in a normal distribution, plus and minus 3σ from the mean will include 9973 cases. All but 3 cases will fall within 5σ above and below the mean.

The area under a frequency polygon represents the total number of cases in the distribution. Knowing the total area, it is possible to compute the chances that a score will fall in any portion of the total area. (See Table XXXII, page 392, in Bovard, Cozens, Hagman; or page 442 in Clarke.)

SKEWNESS

In a "skewed" distribution the mean, median, and mode are at different points and the balance of the graph is thrown to the left or to the right.

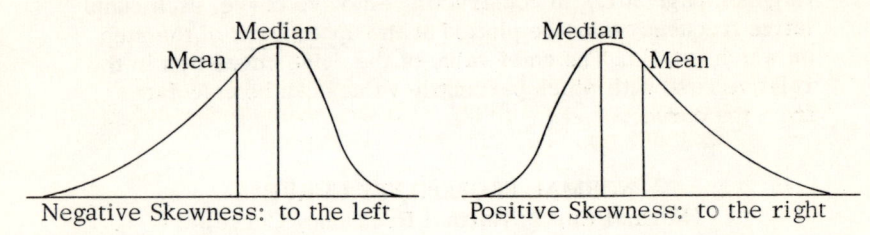

Negative Skewness: to the left   Positive Skewness: to the right

The degree of skewness of a distribution is measured by the formula:

$$\text{Skewness} = \frac{3(\text{mean} - \text{median})}{\sigma}$$

Skewness results from taking too few cases, special selection, or a real lack of "normality" in the data. When the mean and median are equal, the skewness = 0. The marks of graduate students usually give a skewed distribution.

ASSIGNMENT No. 8

(a) Construct a frequency polygon for High Jump (Data I), using 2 as the length of interval for High Jump and 1 for frequency.

(b) Construct a histogram for Broad Jump (Data I), using 6 as the length of interval for Broad Jump and 1 for frequency.

(c) Construct a bar diagram, using the following data:
Number of Freshmen = 40
Number of Sophomores = 28
Number of Juniors = 20
Number of Seniors = 16 .
For frequency, use 3 for length of step.

(d) Construct an ogive curve for High Jump (Data I), using 2 as the length of interval and starting with 32 inches as the beginning of the first step. For frequency, use 2 as length of step.

(e) In a normal frequency curve, what percentage of the cases falls between the mean and .68 of a sigma? Out of 10,000 cases, how many cases will fall between plus and minus .52 of a σ ? When there are 1000 cases in the distribution, how many cases will fall above 2.16 σ? With 10,000 cases in the distribution, what percentage of the cases will fall outside of plus and minus .94 σ ?

(f) Find the amount and direction of skewness for Weight, 100-yard, and Broad Jump, in Data I, using means and σ's computed from Crude Scores.

III. Development of Measurement in Physical Education (Historical Background)

References. Bovard, Cozens, Hagman, pages 17-38; Clarke, pages 3-26.

The five main stages in the development of measurement work in physical education are:
  (1) Anthropometric
  (2) Strength
  (3) Cardiac functional
  (4) Athletic ability
  (5) Single test or index figure

People in India, Egypt, Greece, Rome, Germany and Belgium studied in one way or another the relative proportions of the human body. Sculptors in Greece searched for a unit of measurement that could be used in determining the correct proportions of the perfect man. A rough sort of anthropometry has been used by artists and sculptors down through the centuries.

In 1860 Cromwell studied the growth of Manchester school children, ages 8 to 18, and found the general law that "girls are taller and heavier than boys from the approximate ages of 11 to 14." In 1861 Hitchcock at Amherst made many anthropometric measurements. In 1880 Dr. Sargent at Harvard began measuring students. As far as physical education is concerned, the greater part of the anthropometric work placed emphasis on symmetry and size. This emphasis shifted about 1880 to the actual work that an individual could do, i.e., to strength tests.

Sargent's strength test idea was first worked out in 1873 while at Yale. His conclusion "that body size and measurement of muscles alone do not furnish sufficient data upon which to base a judgment of a man's power and working capacity" remained the dominant idea in physical education for more than 20 years. Strength tests were revived by F. R. Rogers, who stated that they are measures of general athletic ability and can be used to classify boys for competition.

Mosso, the Italian physiologist, was a pioneer in establishing the relationship between "physical condition" and "muscular activity." Physical educators then turned from strength testing to tests of physical condition (functional tests).

Crampton, in 1905, published results of experimentation and devised a rating scheme for changes in cardiac rate and arterial pressure on assuming the erect position.

Development of Measurement

Schneider, after much experimentation, found Crampton's and Foster's tests unsatisfactory and developed one of his own which contained more factors. It is necessary, in order for muscular activities to be at their best, that nutrition, circulation, and the nervous system be in good condition, i.e., the ability to perform may be considerably modified by condition.

The public schools took up the movement of testing for skill in various activities. The City of Detroit, Stecher, the California Decathlon, Reilly, McCurdy, and others made contributions in this field. Several universities since 1910 have used various types of tests with students of college grade. The interest of college women in the testing movement has come about for the most part since 1920. A great many indices of various kinds have been devised.

Recent developments include cardiovascular tests, posture scales, classification of pupils, measurement of general qualities, achievement scales, sport technique tests, knowledge tests, behavior rating scales, health knowledge tests, and width-weight tables.

ASSIGNMENT No. 9

(a) Name the five stages of measurement work in physical education.

(b) Who is regarded as the father of anthropometry in the United States?

(c) What significant contributions were made by the following: Sargent, Baldwin, Crampton, Reilly, and Schneider?

(d) What hastened the shift of emphasis from symmetry and size to measurement of the work done by an individual?

(e) What idea caused a decline in the use of strength tests?

(f) Who invented the ergograph?

(g) What three so-called physical efficiency tests were reported in 1914?

(h) Whose Cardiac Functional Test was widely used in aviation in World War I? What was it used for?

(i) Why did intercollegiate athletics refuse to have anything to do with the strength tests?

(j) When were the athletic badge tests for boys first published? By whom were they published?

32 Statistics, Tests and Measurements in Physical Education

(k) Who worked out the California Decathlon Tests?

(l) In classifying pupils, what three factors are being widely used?

(m) What magazine is the best source for tests and measurements in physical education?

IV. Need for Tests in Physical Education

Reference: Bovard, Cozens, Hagman, pages 3-16.

Physical educators are vitally concerned with pupil development and adjustment which result from activity. We are concerned with ideas, knowledge, and judgments; attitudes, interests, emotions, and ideals; strength and skill; and with the development of organic power and resistance to fatigue.

Measurement is necessary if we are to know the extent of child development. Teachers now judge pupil achievement and progress largely subjectively. If they are to proceed scientifically, they must become acquainted with scientific procedures in constructing tests, setting standards, classifying students, and measuring achievement.

Marks (grades) in physical education are given to pupils. These are based on the teacher's subjective opinion as to the child's attendance, effort, attitude, conduct, and achievement in physical education skills. Each one of these factors is judged on a different basis and the judgments are then added to form the final mark. Marks are useful forces in motivation. Pupils in general like to do better than they did before, and better than their fellows do. Competition offers incentive to improvement. Honors may be given to those who meet certain goals.

Records of the progress of pupils should be kept. The progress of pupils is difficult to measure because of differences in age, experience, and opportunity. Standardized tests should be given to aid the teacher in making judgments.

Classes in physical education are usually organized on a grade basis for elementary schools, and on a class basis for secondary schools. In the high school class, great differences exist among pupils in age, height, weight, capacity, ability, and achievement. It is little fun for the skillful player to compete against the "dub."

The physical education teacher should diagnose the needs of pupils. The remedial program should follow a diagnostic program. Without actual knowledge of defects, remedial teaching may be non-effective.

The field of physical education is rich with opportunities for valuable research. We need research on the efficiency of various methods of instruction, on the progress of pupils, the physiological effects of different types of activities, and the evaluation of the entire school program in physical education.

In order to justify the money we spend, the plants we build, the personnel we employ, and the programs we provide, it is essential that we evaluate objectively and accurately. Tests and measurements help us in evaluating, and they should be geared to objectives.

Six important purposes and uses of tests and measurements are:

1. Diagnostic. To determine differences and to measure fundamental abilities, aptitudes, interests, and needs of pupils.

2. Classification. To assign pupils to activities which they need; to form homogeneous groups.

3. Measure achievement. To measure the pupils' achievement and progress in physical education activities.

4. Administrative. To determine pupil marks objectively. To evaluate results obtained from facilities, activities, and methods of instruction.

5. Supervisory. To rate teachers and evaluate their teaching efficiency.

6. Research. To investigate problems in physical education; to carry on experiments.

ASSIGNMENT No. 10

(a) Is the physical education teacher concerned more directly with the growth of the child or his development? Why?

(b) Why is objective measurement to be preferred to subjective evaluation?

(c) What factors should be considered in giving a pupil a mark (grade) for physical education? How can a pupil's mark, which is a composite of several factors, be determined on a scientific basis?

(d) How can the progress of pupils be determined and shown?

(e) Can the physical education teacher determine all the facts needed for a rather complete diagnosis of the pupil's activity needs? Explain.

Need for Tests   35

(f) Can the efficiency of teachers be determined accurately from the progress of their pupils?

(g) List 10 specific problems in physical education which you think need careful research and which, if solved, would advance the field as a whole. Each sentence should be a complete sentence and end with a question mark.

V. Terminology and Classification of Tests

References. Brace, David K.: The Classification of Tests in Physical Education. American Physical Education Review, December 1926.

A report of the Committee on Terminology in Measurement in Physical Education with Special Reference to Classification, American Physical Education Review, September 1929. Committee composed of James G. Bliss, S. C. Staley, David K. Brace.

DEFINITION OF TERMS

(Some of the definitions have been modified.)

1. Measurement. A process of objective evaluation.
2. Ability. Developed power to perform any act; the highest performance to date; capacity that has been developed through activity.
3. Accuracy. Freedom from errors.
4. Achievement. The evaluation of performance in terms of what other pupils in the classified group can do.
5. Anthropometric. Bodily measurements of people relating to structure.
6. Antero-posterior posture. Posture as seen from the side.
7. Battery of tests. A series of tests given to a group of pupils at one time or within a short period of time.
8. Capacity. The limits (potential) set by heredity and other factors within which ability may be developed through activities.
9. Calipers. An instrument for measuring bodily depths and breadths.
10. Chest expansion. Difference in girth of chest with one measurement taken after full expiration and one taken following a full inspiration.
11. Chronological age. Age in years, months, and days from time of birth.
12. Coefficient of reliability. The "r" between scores obtained from two applications of the same or equivalent tests separated by only a short interval of time; .90 is acceptable and relatively high.

Terminology and Classification of Tests

13. <u>Coefficient of validity</u>. The "r" between test scores and some criterion by which the validity of the test is being judged.
14. <u>Comparable measures</u>. Measures expressed in terms of the same unit and with reference to the same zero.
15. <u>Control group</u>. A group not subjected to the experimental procedures.
16. <u>Correlation</u>. The relationship between two or more series of measures of the same individuals.
17. <u>Criterion</u>. A law, fact, or standard by which the validity of some factor is to be determined.
18. <u>Data</u>. Facts that are used as sources of information.
19. <u>Decathlon test</u>. A test consisting of ten events.
20. <u>Deciles</u>. Points that divide the total number of cases in a frequency distribution into ten equal parts.
21. <u>Dynamometer</u>. An instrument for measuring muscular strength.
22. <u>Experimental group</u>. The group subjected to the experimental procedures.
23. <u>Health</u>. Freedom from disease; a condition enabling the body to function efficiently; a quality of functioning of the human organism.
24. <u>Mark</u>. Refers to the rating given pupils (to be preferred to grade).
25. <u>Motor ability</u>. Developed general ability to move the body or parts of the body in different planes.
26. <u>Objective</u>. (1) A goal, aim, or purpose. (2) Accurate test scores. A test is objective when <u>different</u> examiners, using it to measure the same thing, obtain the same scores.
27. <u>Performance</u>. A pupil's performance is what he does; four feet in the high jump is a performance record.
28. <u>Pulse test</u>. A test which indicates the reaction of the pulse to activity or other conditions.
29. <u>Quality scale</u>. A scale composed of a set of samples arranged in order of merit. The <u>Brownell</u> scale for measuring posture is an example.
30. <u>Questionnaire</u>. A series of questions used in the collection of educational data. The questionnaire should be used only when there is no other available source from which to obtain the needed data.
31. <u>Random sample</u>. A sample that has been selected without bias from the total group which it is to represent.

32. <u>Rank correlation</u>. A method of finding relationship by computing "r" between ranks rather than exact scores.
33. <u>Raw score</u>. The unit used in scoring the test.
34. <u>Reliable</u>. The degree to which a second application of a test, by the <u>same examiner</u>, yields scores equivalent to those obtained from the first application.
35. <u>Standard</u>. A statement of the goal which pupils should reach at a certain time. Standards are different from norms.
36. <u>Standardized test</u>. A test for which satisfactory norms have been established.
37. <u>Statistical method</u>. A method of research based on the collection and analysis of numerical data.
38. <u>Subjective</u>. When different results are obtained by different persons, or the same person at different times, when trying to measure the same thing.
39. <u>T-Scale</u>. A statistical scale proposed by McCall and named in honor of Terman and Thorndike. The scale is based upon the average or normal distribution of ability of 12-year-old pupils. It consists of 100 units, running from 0 to 100, each score being .1 of a standard deviation; it extends from 5σ's below the mean to 5σ's above the mean. The mean score is therefore always approximately 50 on the scale. The T-scale provides a means of comparing scores derived from different tests.
40. <u>Undistributed scores</u>. Scores that fail to distinguish between degrees of pupil abilities. Example: Zero scores in pull-up.
41. <u>Validity</u>. A test has validity when it really measures what it claims to measure.
42. <u>Weighting</u>. The assigning of values to be played by each of a number of items when determining a total or average score.
43. <u>Zero point</u>. The point of origin on a scale which indicates that just not any of the trait is measured by the scale. The zero used on most educational tests does not represent the <u>true</u> zero. Examples: pull-up, basketball throw for goal.

Terminology and Classification of Tests   39

CLASSIFICATION OF TESTS

A study of the literature reveals a lack of uniformity in the terms used in physical education tests and measurements. A common agreement on terms is fundamental. If every worker coins a new name for his test, greater confusion will result. The following terms have been used; those with a "[1]" should be discarded. Why?

1. Ability Tests
    a. Athletic
    [1]b. General
    c. General Athletic
    d. Motor
    [1]e. Native
    [1]f. Native Motor
    [1]g. Physical
2. Achievement
3. Agility
4. Anthropometric (measurements)
5. Aptitude
6. Attitude
[1]7. Badge
8. Balance
9. Capacity
    [1]a. Physical
    b. Sensory
    c. Organic
10. Character
11. Condition
    [1]a. Physical
    b. Physiological
12. Conduct
13. Decathlon
14. Efficiency
    a. Cardiac
    [1]b. Functional
    [1]c. Physical
    d. Organic
15. Endurance
[1]16. Energy
17. Health
18. Knowledge
19. Motor Accomplishment
20. Motor Control
21. Neuromuscular Control
22. Organic Power
23. Performance
[1]24. Physical Fitness
[1]25. Physical Intelligence
26. Play Interests
27. Posture
28. Practice
[1]29. Proficiency
30. Respiratory
31. Skill
32. Speed
33. Strength
34. Technique Tests

Tests may be classified according to:
1. Type or kind of activity measured (basketball).
2. Method employed in constructing the test (true-false).
3. Purpose for which the test is designed (achievement).
4. Function that the test performs (diagnostic).

A test may fall under more than one classification, depending upon its function. All examinations and tests are of structural and functional traits or powers. Anthropometric measurements are of structural traits. Tests of function relate to the functional traits or powers, i.e., (1) interpretive traits, (2) impulsive traits, (3) neuromuscular traits, (4) organic traits.

Recommended classifications of tests in physical education are:

A. General classification
  1. Anthropometric measurements
  2. Capacity tests
  3. Performance tests
  4. Ability tests
  5. Achievement tests
  6. Attitude tests
  7. Health tests
  8. Organic tests
  9. Efficiency tests

B. Classification of tests of functions
  1. Interpretive tests--knowledge, judgment
  2. Impulsive tests--interests, attitudes, emotions, ideals
  3. Neuromuscular tests--strength, skills
  4. Organic tests--circulatory power, respiratory power

VI. Methods of Scoring Tests

References

    Cozens, F. W.: Test Scoring in Physical Education, <u>Journal of Health and Physical Education</u>. December, 1930

    Bovard, Cozens, and Hagman: <u>Tests and Measurements in Physical Education</u>, 3rd edition, pages 309-324

    McCall, William A.: <u>How To Measure in Education</u>, Chapters IX and X

    McCloy, C. H.: A Statistical and Mathematical Method of Devising Athletic Scoring Tables, <u>American Physical Education Review</u>, Vol. 26:1, January, 1921

    Brace, David K.: A Method for Constructing Athletic Scoring Tables, <u>American Physical Education Review</u>, Vol. 29:4, April, 1924

The <u>purpose and use</u> of a scale, the range of ability to be measured, and the meaning of particular point values (including zero point) are important items in scale building.

1. Is the scale to be used for showing pupil progress, for purposes of motivation, as a means of determining a final mark, or as a means of awarding honors?

2. Is the scale to be used as a means of classifying boys and girls for purposes of instruction?

3. Is the attainment of a given standard our only consideration?

4. Is the plan of scoring such that all points on the scale have an equal value?
    What is the meaning of the zero point, the 100-point or 50-point value, and are these points so located that they represent the same relative performance on the scale for every individual and for every test?

5. Does the scale lack motivation above and below a certain set standard?

6. Is it possible to reward inferior performances, or are only performances at average or above average rewarded?

7. Are the performance levels so far apart that fine distinctions in ability within each group are impossible?

8. Should the scale be so arranged that intervals at the peak of performance are rewarded with a larger number of points?

42   Statistics, Tests and Measurements in Physical Education

Classes or groups may be formed by using σ's or quartiles or percentiles. The percentile scale shows the position of an individual in a group on the basis of that portion of the group that he exceeds. The percentile scale makes the assumption that the difference in distance, on a linear scale, between 10% and 20% is the same as the distance between 50% and 60%. This assumption is difficult to defend and, consequently, while the scale is very practical it is unsound in theory and hence should not be used.

SIGMA INDEX SCORES
(Standard Scores or Measures)

Standard scores are found by dividing the deviations from the mean by the standard deviation.

Sigma Index or Standard Measure $= \dfrac{X - M}{\sigma_x} = \dfrac{x}{\sigma_x}$

Standard measures found for the same person on different events can be added for a composite score. See Bovard, Cozens, Hagman, pages 314-316.

T-Score Scales

T-scores are based on the σ of the distribution and usually range from 0 to 100. The mean can be called 50 or 100 or any other number. The base line is divided into 10 σ's. When the mean is taken as 50, five σ's will equal 50, or one σ = 10. Then σ_x is the σ of the distribution.

The T-score on the scale $= \dfrac{x}{\sigma_x} \times (10) + 50$ (formula)

Example. Find the T-score for case 3 in the weight distribution in Data I.

Given: X = _____
        M_x = _____   The score =
        σ_x = _____ $\dfrac{x}{\sigma_x} \times (10) + 50 =$ _____
        x = _____

The T-scale units are equal at all points on the scale. T-scores on various tests can be added as they are comparable.

Methods of Scoring Tests

INCREASED INCREMENT SCALE

The increased increment scale is an attempt to devise a method by which increasingly difficult performances are rewarded by increasingly greater scores. It has been recognized that as an individual approaches the limit of his capacity in a given activity in which he is being tested, he finds greater difficulty in improving his performance. Thus, the 10-second man has greater difficulty in reducing his time to 9.5 seconds than the 13-second man has in reducing his time to 12.5 seconds, always assuming that the differences in initial performance are due to the effects of training, etc., and not to inherent differences in capacity. The graphic representation of such a scale is not a straight line, but is some sort of a parabolic curve that starts upward from the base-line slowly, and increases more rapidly as the distance between the base-line and the curve widens.

ASSIGNMENT No. 11

(a) What is the zero point in basketball goal-throwing when using 10 trials?

(b) How can you tell whether or not a test is too easy?

(c) What is wrong with the success-or-failure method of scoring a test?

(d) Make a list of the crude scores for High Jump, Data I. Taking the mean (found by the crude score method) to the nearest two decimal places, make a second column opposite the scores showing the standard scores for the 25 cases.

(e) 1. Find the T-score for case 10 for weight, using the crude score method of finding the mean and σ. On the T-scale, let the mean equal 100, and divide the base line into 10 σs.

    2. Find the T-score for case 15 for weight when the mean is taken as 50 and the base-line is divided into 6 sigmas.

$$\frac{x}{\sigma_x} \times (16\tfrac{2}{3}) + 50 = \underline{\qquad\qquad}$$

Statistics, Tests and Measurements in Physical Education

does not affect self-correlation but does introduce a constant error. Much of the early statistical work in education was of doubtful value because of the failure to compute reliability.

VIII. Analysis of Some Existing Tests

Three projects are to be completed:
A. Each student will be assigned one or more tests for an oral report to the class.
B. All students will read, study, and abstract the information about certain tests which seem to be of major importance. These tests will be discussed in class.
C. Class members will be assigned to small committees, and each committee will demonstrate an important test in class.

Note: Each student is to keep a separate notebook, in handwriting, on projects A, B, and C. This notebook will be marked on its quality at the end of the course.

Outline for Each Abstract

Each abstract should cover the following essential points:
1. Subject of the report and the complete reference.
2. A statement of the problem.
3. Method that the author used in attacking the problem; i.e., experimental, analytical, questionnaire, etc.
4. Pertinent facts submitted in solving the problem.
5. Author's conclusions and recommendations.
6. Your personal evaluation of the study; how it might be used in a school program.

INDIVIDUAL ORAL REPORTS

(Note to student: Use additional references wherever possible.)

1. A Scale for Measuring the Antero-Posterior Posture of Ninth Grade Boys, by C. L. Brownell. T. C. Contributions to Education, No. 325. 1928
2. Pryor's Width-Weight Tables. Ref: Larson and Yocom, pages 125-127, 137
3. Crampton's "Blood Ptosis" Test. Ref: Bovard, Cozens, and Hagman, page 64
4. Meylan's Test. Ref: Bovard, Cozens, and Hagman, pages 65-66
5. Foster's Test. Ref: Bovard, Cozens, and Hagman, pages 66-67

6. Effect of Strenuous Exertion upon the Heart Rate. Ref: Cureton, pages 182-183

7. Effect of Exercise upon the Heart. Ref: Cureton, pages 311-319

8. Sargent's Test. Ref: Bovard, Cozens, and Hagman, pages 124-125

9. Recent Studies in the Sargent Jump. Ref, Research Quarterly, May 1932, pages 235-242

10. A Method of Testing Strength of the Abdominal Muscles. Ref: A. P. E. Review, June 1924, page 343

11. The Apparent Importance of Arm Strength in Athletics. Ref: Research Quarterly, March 1934, pages 3-11

12. The Significance of Strength Tests in Revealing Physical Condition. Ref: Research Quarterly, October 1934, pages 43-46

13. The Inadequacy of Strength Norms. Ref: Research Quarterly, December 1935, pages 117-124

14. Equating Opponents in Sports. Ref: Research Quarterly, March (Supplement) 1935, pages 189-226

15. The Measurement of General Athletic Ability in College Men. Ref: University of Oregon Publication, 1929. Bovard, Cozens and Hagman, pages 156-158

16. Measuring Reaction Time of Athletes. Ref: Research Quarterly, March 1936, pages 110-118

17. The Measurement of Achievement in Physical Education. Ref: A. P. E. Review, October 1927, page 563

18. Achievement Tests in Volleyball for High School Girls. Ref: Research Quarterly, May 1937, pages 150-157

19. California Decathlon Charts. Ref: Bovard, Cozens, and Hagman, page 93 (folder on Tests)

20. Reilly's Rational Athletics for Boys and Girls. Ref: Bovard, Cozens, and Hagman, page 92

21. The Influence of Chronological Age on Motor Performance. Ref: Research Quarterly, May 1935, pages 61-64

Analysis of Some Existing Tests 49

22. Information Tests in Health and Physical Education for High School Boys. Ref: Research Quarterly, December 1932, pages 83-96
23. Comprehensive Tennis Knowledge Test. Ref: Research Quarterly, October 1937, pages 74-84
24. A Health Knowledge Test. Ref: Research Quarterly, May 1935, pages 105-120
25. Wetzel Grid for Measurement of Physique and Development. Ref: Larson and Yocom, pages 127-133; Bovard, Cozens, and Hagman, page 53
26. The Schneider Test. Ref: Larson and Yocom, page 65; Bovard, Cozens, and Hagman, pages 69-71
27. Meaning of Pulse Rate. Ref: Cureton, pages 162-164
28. Motor Fitness Tests. Ref: Cureton, pages 48-54
29. Vital Capacity as an Index of Fitness. Ref: Cureton, pages 334-341
30. Tests of Balance. Ref: McCloy and Young, pages 103-107; Bovard, Cozens, and Hagman, pages 163-166
31. Tests of Rhythm. Ref: McCloy and Young, pages 107-108; Bovard, Cozens, and Hagman, pages 200-202
32. Measurement of Individual Adjustment. Ref: Larson and Yocom, pages 252-267

CLASS ABSTRACTS

I. Anthropometric Measurements

Some of the values of anthropometric measurements are:
(a) As a basis for classification for instruction and competition.
(b) As a diagnostic factor in the prescription of activity.
(c) As a criterion for evaluation of the nutritional status of the individual.
(d) As a motivating factor in the promotion of interest in activities.
(e) As a record of progress made in growth. Measurements of height, weight, breadth, depth, girth, proportion, and vital capacity are made in objective units because of such tools as scales, tape measure, stadiometer, calipers, silhouetteograph, and spirometer.

1. Anthropometric Measurements. Ref: Bovard, Cozens, and Hagman, pages 39-61
2. Posture and Foot Measurement. Ref: Clarke, pages 148-181
3. Appraisal of Body Type. Ref: Cureton, pages 69-133

II. Medical and Sensory Tests
4. Medical and Sensory Tests. Ref: Clarke, pages 66-93

III. Cardiac Functional Tests

The fundamental problem in cardiac functional testing is to determine the condition of the heart and circulation at rest compared with the condition following specific kinds and amounts of exercise. The reaction of the cardiovascular system to exercise may be taken as a reliable criterion of an individual's organic condition.

A complete heart examination would include:
(a) Pulse rate lying, sitting, and standing, before and after a controlled amount of exercise.
(b) Diastolic and systolic blood pressures lying, sitting, and standing, before and after exercise.
(c) Auscultatory examination of heart and significance of heart sounds.
(d) An X-ray or fluoroscopic picture of heart.
(e) Electrocardiograms with an interpretation of their meaning.

For school children we need a simple, inexpensive, and easily administered test that can be given by the physical education teacher. Special cases may be referred to the physician for examination. Some type of pulse-rate test seems most satisfactory.

5. Physiological Fitness. Ref: Clarke, pages 94-119
6. Tests of Endurance. Ref: McCloy and Young, pages 165-192

IV. Motor Fitness
7. Motor Fitness Tests. Ref. Clarke, pages 221-241
8. Strength as an Index of Fitness. Ref: Cureton, pages 356-386
9. Tests of General Motor Capacity. Ref: McCloy and Young, pages 114-126

V. Strength Tests

The invention of the spirometer and of various types of

Analysis of Some Existing Tests 51

manometers and dynamometers gave emphasis to the development of strength tests. Dudley Sargent was a pioneer in this field. Up to a point, we may look for an increase in strength with an increase in skill. The measurement of strength is a better single index of what an individual can do than is the measurement of proportions, but strength alone does not ensure skill in performance. The weight lifter is strong, but not necessarily skillful in sport activities.

In reviving the strength test, F. R. Rogers acknowledged the work of Dudley A. Sargent who first recognized the relationship between muscular strength and the physical education program. Rogers has said:

> Physical education is misdirected; highly trained teams; games with little carry-over value; those who need it most get least attention; remedy lies in redirection. We must insist on equality of abilities between competing individuals or groups. Progress toward any remote goal depends upon measurements. A measurement program is not a substitute for skillful teaching. General athletic ability involves intelligence, motor skills, courage, perseverance, cooperation, and strength. No amount of knowledge, skill, or courage will avail if the athlete lacks muscular power (strength). The <u>Strength Index</u> is a valid measure of <u>general</u> athletic ability. It is over $2\frac{1}{2}$ times as accurate as weight, and nearly twice as accurate as the best combination of age, height, and weight. By far the most important measure of athletic ability is speed in running.

10. Strength Tests. Ref: Clarke, pages 182-220

VI. Ability and Achievement Tests

The performance of a pupil is not necessarily an indication of his present ability or his <u>native</u> capacity. Performance is dependent upon a number of variables:

(1) effort
(2) interest
(3) motivation
(4) emotional status
(5) organic condition
(6) weather
(7) time of day
(8) personality of examiner
(9) directions for test
(10) pupil's knowledge of test
(11) time allowed for test

At present, we cannot accurately measure native motor capacity. Hence, for an estimate, we must rely upon the results shown in the performance of our pupils. In the final analysis these results will depend upon the native motor capacity possessed by the pupil, plus the effects of instruction, experience, and practice.

By many writers the terms capacity and ability are used interchangeably as synonyms and without due regard to the difference in meaning of the two words. The term capacity means potential, or the limits within which abilities can be developed. The term ability indicates the actual amount to which capacity has been developed through activity. Thus an individual probably will have greater capacity than he has ability.

Achievement tests may be given prior to and following a course of instruction for the purpose of determining the amount of progress which has been made during the intervening time. Performance records are transmuted into achievement scores by use of an achievement scale derived from the performances of a homogeneous group of persons. The best performance record or achievement score made to date may be taken as the person's known ability.

Probably the fundamental qualities which an individual should possess to ensure his success in physical education activities are: interest, speed, endurance, strength, coordination, balance, orientation (in tumbling, dancing, etc.) and intelligence. Fundamental to these qualities is the assumption that the individual will be free from:
  (1) organic defects of the cardiovascular, respiratory, and other organic systems of the body; and
  (2) defects such as defective hearing and vision, structural defects which impair breathing, and muscular-skeletal defects resulting in poor body mechanics.

11. Skill Tests. Ref: Clark, pages 324-355
12. Ref: Neilson, N. P. and Cozens, F. W. Achievement Scales in Physical Education Activities for Boys and Girls in Elementary and Junior High Schools. California State Department of Education, Sacramento, California, 1934. 177 pages

Analysis of Some Existing Tests 53

VII. Knowledge Tests (Information)
   13. Knowledge Tests. Ref: Clarke, pages 356-374
   14. Knowledge and Information Tests. Ref: Bovard, Cozens, and Hagman, pages 219-233.

VIII. Social Efficiency Tests
   15. Physical Education and Social Efficiency. Ref: Clarke, pages 245-278
   16. Character Education and Physical Education. Ref: McCloy and Young, pages 12; 277-287

COMMITTEE REPORTS

These reports are to be demonstrations of sample tests in the four areas of function, tests which seem practical in an elementary school or high school situation.

General References
   A. McCloy and Carpenter. Laboratory Manual for Tests and Measurements in Health and Physical Education, New York: F. S. Crofts and Co., 1941. 140 pages
   B. Weiss and Phillips. Administration of Tests in Physical Education. St. Louis: The C. V. Mosby Company, 1954. 278 pages
   C. Hunsaker and Montoye. Applied Tests and Measurements in Physical Education, Englewood Cliffs, New Jersey: Prentice-Hall, Inc., 1953, 149 pages

Reports

I. Interpretive Function (knowledge, judgment)
   1. Physical Education Knowledge Tests. (volleyball, soccer, basketball, golf, tennis, baseball) Ref: Research Quarterly: October 1935; March 1936; May 1936, pages 77-91
   2. Health Knowledge of High School and College Students. Ref: Research Quarterly, October 1937, pages 3-32

54   Statistics, Tests and Measurements in Physical Education

  II. <u>Impulsive Function</u> (interests, attitudes, emotions)
- 3. <u>Carr Attitude Scale</u>. Weiss and Phillips, page 43
- 4. <u>Blanchard Behavior Rating Scale</u>. Weiss and Phillips, page 41
- 5. <u>Behavior Rating Scale</u>. McCloy and Carpenter, pages 115-120
- 6. <u>Rating of Character</u>. McCloy and Carpenter, pages 109-114

III. <u>Neuromuscular Function</u> (strength and skill)
- 7. Rogers Strength Index. <u>Tests and Measurement Programs in the Redirection of Physical Education</u>, by F. R. Rogers. Bureau of Publications, Teachers College, Columbia University, New York City, 1927, 166 pages. Also, Weiss and Phillips, pages 179-190

- 8. <u>MacEwan-Howe Posture Test</u>. Weiss and Phillips, pages 29-33

- 9. <u>Tests of Balance</u>. McCloy and Carpenter, pages 49-51

- 10. "Brace Motor Ability," by David K. Brace. <u>Measuring Motor Ability</u>, New York, A. S. Barnes and Company, 1927, 133 pages. Also, Weiss and Phillips, pages 68-72

- 11. <u>Measures of Agility</u>. McCloy and Carpenter, pages 19-21

- 12. <u>Cozens' General Athletic Ability Test</u>. Weiss and Phillips, pages 75-97

- 13. <u>Lehsten Basketball Test</u>. Weiss and Phillips, pages 207-212.

- 14. <u>French-Cooper Volleyball Test</u>. Weiss and Phillips, pages 269-274

- 15. Achievement Scales. Cozens, Trieb and Neilson. <u>Physical Education Achievement Scales for Boys in Secondary Schools</u>. New York: A. S. Barnes and Company, 1936, 155 pages

- 16. Achievement Scales. Cozens, Cubberley and Neilson. <u>Achievement Scales in Physical Education Activities for Secondary School Girls and College Women</u>. New York: A. S. Barnes and Company, 1937, 165 pages

- 17. Youth Fitness Tests. Manual by American Association for Health, Physical Education and Recreation, 1958, 64 pages

Analysis of Some Existing Tests 55

IV. Organic Function (endurance, resistance to fatigue)
17. Tuttle Pulse Ratio Test. Larson and Yocom, page 67; also Bovard, Cozens and Hagman, pages 73-76
18. McCurdy-Larson Organic Efficiency Test. Larson and Yocom, page 69; also Bovard, Cozens and Hagman, pages 78-79
19. Endurance. McCloy and Carpenter, pages 47-48
20. Burpee Test. Weiss and Phillips, pages 131-132

IX. Test Construction in Physical Education

References. Bovard, Cozens and Hagman, pages 339-365; and McCloy and Young, pages 29-36

The important criteria to be kept in mind in the choice of tests and in the construction of tests are: (1) validity, (2) reliability, (3) objectivity, (4) administrative economy, (5) the use of norms, (6) duplicate forms, and (7) standardized directions.

The first step in constructing a test is to determine the quality to be measured. Other steps in the process of test construction are:
1. Selection of test items
2. Choice of criteria for establishing validity
3. Preliminary tryout to standardize directions
4. Securing reliability of simple tests
5. Elimination of test items
6. Secure an adequate criterion score
7. Control of experimental conditions
8. Selection of final battery
9. Determination of battery reliability
10. Preparation of a manual for use in administering the test battery.

ASSIGNMENT No. 12

1. When is a test valid? How can validity be determined?
2. When is a test reliable? How can reliability be determined?
3. What is the effect of test length on reliability?
4. What effect does reliability have on validity?
5. What should the reliability coefficient be to be considered high?
6. When is a test objective?
7. In administrative economy, what two factors must be considered?
8. How can good norms be established?
9. What are the conditions to be met if duplicate forms of a test are to be equivalent?
10. What are some of the possible directions which should be given in a high jump test?

11. Name several ways of validating physical education tests.

ASSIGNMENT No. 13

1. Construct a T-Scale for Class "B' Boys in an Elementary School.

   Given: Event = Jump and Reach
   Mean = 10.42 inches
   Sigma = 1.42 inches
   Let the mean = a T-Score of 50
   Use 10 sigmas on the base line
   Let each T-Score = .1 standard deviation
   Let the T-Scale range from 0 to 100

2. A boy did 12.25 inches in the Jump and Reach. What was his T-Score on your scale?

3. A boy got a T-Score of 30; what was his performance in the Jump and Reach?

ASSIGNMENT No. 14

1. Construct a T-Scale for Archery at 30 yards, using 3 sigmas on each side of the mean; let mean equal a T-Score of 50; in scale, round off archery points to the nearest whole number. Archery scores: 110, 54, 72, 116, 66, 51, 132, 63, 104, 82, 85, 68, 130, 80, 62, 108, 70, 108, 99, 64, 107, 125, 51, 50, 105, 60, 80, 60, 114, 120, 78, 105, 68, 60, 84, 99, 76, 36, 54, 50, 102, 70, 104, 57, 62, 64, 67, 74, 17, 60, 122, 125, 85, 62, 72, 147, 96, 64, 60, 98, 74, 50, 78, 133, 103, 90, 102, 38, 58, 84, 60, 69, 75, 85, 52, 86, 52, 102, 72, 50, 78, 70, 108, 64, 74, 72, 149, 98, 72, 69, 83, 108, 64, 60, 53, 106, 121, 74, 84, 106.

   What is the mean?
   What is the sigma?
   With 3 sigmas on each side of mean, a T-score will equal .06 of the sigma. (Place scale on one sheet of paper.)

Achievement Scale - Junior College Girls - Archery at 30 Yards

Score	Points in Archery	Score	Points in Archery
100		50	
99		49	
etc.		etc.	

X. Test Administration

References

<u>Program Organization and Test Administration.</u> Ref: Bovard, Cozens and Hagman, pages 366-381
<u>Administrative Problems.</u> Ref: Clarke, pages 377-419

In the administration of any test, the analysis of the results obtained is of the greatest importance and value. Collection of data that are never used is a waste of time. Under most circumstances a specified test will serve only one major purpose--that for which the test was designed. It is a mistake to administer a standardized test in a careless manner, or to misinterpret the data obtained.

In giving tests to physical education students, time must be conserved. It is unwise to have large numbers of students standing about, sometimes for the whole period, waiting for their turn to be tested. The directions for giving the tests must be clear and exact.

The guiding principles in the preparation of instructions are:

1. They should be brief, yet clear.
2. A preliminary or demonstration test should be used.
3. They should be uniform for all who are tested.
4. The order of instructions should be the order of doing.
5. Instructions should equalize interest.
6. Instructions should be given to pupils and examiner.

Facilities used in the testing should be ready. All examiners should be instructed to use uniform procedures. The use of muscles should be alternated to avoid fatigue when taking a battery of tests. Individual blanks or score cards are preferred for recording.

General Bibliography

American Association for Health, Physical Education, and Recreation. Research Methods in Health, Physical Education, Recreation," 2nd ed., 1959, 535 pages

Bliss, James G.; Staley, S. C. and Brace, David K. "A Report of the Committee on Terminology in Measurement in Physical Education with Special Reference to Classification." American Physical Education Review, September 1929

Brace, David K. Measuring Motor Ability. New York: A. S. Barnes and Company, 1927, 138 pages

Brace, David K. "The Classification of Tests in Physical Education. American Physical Education Review, December 1926

Cozens, F. W. Achievement Scales in Physical Education Activities - for College Men. Philadelphia: Lea and Febiger, 1936, 118 pages

Cozens, Frederick W. The Measurement of General Athletic Ability in College Men. Eugene, Oregon: University of Oregon Press, 1929, 192 pages

Cozens, F. W.; Cubberly, Hazel J. and Neilson, N. P. Achievement Scales in Physical Education Activities - for Secondary School Girls and College Women. New York: A. S. Barnes and Company, 1937, 165 pages

Cozens, F. W.; Trieb, M. H. and Neilson, N. P. Physical Education Achievement Scales - for Boys in Secondary Schools. New York: A. S. Barnes and Company, 1936, 155 pages. (May be obtained for $2.00 by writing to Mrs. M. H. Trieb, 330 South Mansfield Ave., Los Angeles 36, Calif.)

Glassow, Ruth B. and Broer, Marion R. Measuring Achievement in Physical Education. Philadelphia: W. B. Saunders Company, 1938, 344 pages

Neilson, N. P. and Arnett, Glenn W. A Score Card for Use in Evaluating Physical Education Programs in Elementary Schools. Salt Lake City: University of Utah Press, 1955, 53 pages

Neilson, N. P. and Cozens, F. W. Achievement Scales in Physical Education Activities - for Boys and Girls in Elementary and Junior High Schools. California State Department of Education, Sacramento, California, 1934, 177 pages

Neilson, N. P. and Hall, Vaughn L. A Score Card for Use in Evaluation of Physical Education Programs for High School Boys. Salt Lake City: State Department of Public Instruction, 1949, 65 pages

Scott, M. Gladys and French, Esther. Evaluation in Physical Education. St. Louis: C. V. Mosby Company, 1950, 348 pages

Stroup, Francis. Measurement in Physical Education. New York: The Ronald Press Company, 1957, 192 pages

Appendix

REVIEW QUESTIONS

1. Name three recently published textbooks in the field of physical education tests and measurements.
2. How do you make a frequency distribution?
3. How can the range of scores be determined?
4. What is the desirable number of step intervals for a frequency distribution?
5. In tabulating scores, how can errors be avoided?
6. What is the best method of representing scores within a step interval?
7. How do you find the mid-point of a step?
8. Define "Measures of Central Tendency."
9. Name the measures of central tendency.
10. How do you find the mean when scores are ungrouped?
11. How do you find the mean when the scores are grouped?
12. How do you find the mean by the guessed-average method?
13. Define "median."
14. What formula can be used to find the median?
15. Define the mode.
16. How can you tell when a distribution is perfectly normal?
17. Define "Measures of Variability."
18. Name the measures of variability.
19. Define "Range."
20. Define "Quartile Deviation."
21. How can you find Q_3?
22. What percentage of the cases does the range include?
23. What percentage of the cases does one Q on one side of the median include?
24. Define "Average Deviation."
25. From where is the A D usually computed?
26. How do you find a deviation?
27. What percentage of the cases is included within plus and minus one A D?
28. Which is larger, an A D or Q?
29. Define "Standard Deviation."
30. Write the crude score formula for SD.
31. In a normal distribution, how do you find one probable error?
32. What percentage of the cases is included within one probable error on one side of the mean?
33. When does a probable error equal a Q?

34. Extract the square root of 168.42.
35. When should you use the average deviation?
36. When should you use the standard deviation?
37. Why is the obtained mean not the true mean?
38. State the formula for sigma of the mean.
39. What does the probable error of the mean equal?
40. What does the probable error of the mean, mean?
41. What is meant by the standard deviation of the sigma?
42. In a normal distribution of 10,000 cases, how many cases will lie outside of three standard deviations on each side of the mean? Outside of five standard deviations on each side of the mean?
43. Name three measures of relationship.
44. Define "Correlation."
45. Evaluate the following correlations: -.62; 1.74; .89; -2.42 .
46. If you have seven factors, how can you find how many combinations for the factors could be arranged?
47. You have some high jump scores and some broad jump scores; how would you label them?
48. What is meant by a probable error of an "r"?
49. Define "Ordinate."
50. Define "Abscissa."
51. How do you draw a frequency polygon?
52. How do you construct a histogram?
53. How do you construct an ogive curve?
54. If you toss two pennies once, what is the probability?
55. How many cases are found between the mean and plus-and-minus one SD?
56. When is a distribution skewed negatively? Positively?
57. What causes skewness?
58. Name the five stages in the development of measurement work in physical education.
59. What man is noted for the development of strength tests?
60. Name an early American noted for his work in anthropometric measurements.
61. Name a functional test.
62. What did Dr. Schneider do? Reilly? Stolz? Pryor?
63. Who published the athletic badge tests?
64. In classifying pupils, what three factors are being widely used?
65. What magazine rates the best source for tests and measurements in physical education before 1930? Since 1930?
66. Why is measurement necessary in physical education?

67. Name six important uses of tests and measurements in physical education.
68. Why is objective measurement to be preferred over subjective evaluation?
69. Can the efficiency of a teacher be determined accurately from the progress of her pupils?
70. Define: performance; achievement; ability; capacity; progress; accomplishment.
71. Define: battery of tests; chronological age; anatomical age; objectivity; validity; reliability; correlation; data; decil; decathlon test; dynamometer; health.
72. Define: quality scale; random sample; raw score; norm; standard; T-scale; undistributed scores.
73. Give a general classification of tests in physical education.
74. Give a 4-point classification of tests of functions.
75. Why has a scale based on percentages come into disrepute?
76. In constructing T-scales, what measure is used as the common denominator?
77. How would you compute a standard score?
78. What advantage exists in using standard measures?
79. Why is it better to use 6 sigmas rather than 10 sigmas in constructing T-scales?
80. When $X = 142$; $M = 126$; $sigma = 22$; find the T-score, assuming the scale runs from 0 to 100 and using 10 sigmas.
81. What is wrong with the pass-or-fail method of scoring a test?
82. Name 10 important characteristics that a good test should possess.
83. What features tend to make a test unreliable?
84. How can you increase the reliability of a test?
85. How can you find the reliability of a test?
86. Give an abstract of the following tests, including a statement of the problem, method author used in attacking the problem, a few pertinent facts, author's conclusions, and your evaluation of the test:
    a. Brownell's test of posture
    b. Pryor's Width-Weight tables
    c. Cozen's general athletic ability test
    d. Reilly's rational athletics for boys and girls
    e. Cureton on "Appraisal of Body Type"
    f. McCurdy-Larson Test of Organic Efficiency
    g. Rogers P.F.I. (strength test)
    h. Neilson-Cozens "Achievement Scales in Physical Education Activities for Boys and Girls in Elementary and Junior High Schools"

      i. Brace Motor Ability test
      j. Tuttle Pulse ratio test
      k. Burpee test
87. In constructing a test, what is the first step?
88. When is a test valid?
89. When is a test reliable?
90. When is a test objective?
91. What effect does reliability have on validity?
92. To be considered high, how high should a reliability coefficient be?
93. Name three ways of validating a physical education test.
94. Indicate the steps to be used in constructing a T-scale.
95. Indicate some rules to be observed in administering tests.

CLASSIFICATION CHART FOR BOYS AND GIRLS
(Elementary and Junior High)

Exponent	Height in Inches	Age in Years and Months	Weight in Pounds	Sum of Exponents	Class
1	50 to 51	10 to 10-5	60 to 65	9 & below	A
2	52 to 53	10-6 to 10-11	66 to 70	10 to 14	B
3		11 to 11-5	71 to 75	15 to 19	C
4	54 to 55	11-6 to 11-11	76 to 80	20 to 24	D
5		12 to 12-5	81 to 85	25 to 29	E
6	56 to 57	12-6 to 12-11	86 to 90	30 to 34	F
7		13 to 13-5	91 to 95	35 to 38	G
8	58 to 59	13-6 to 13-11	96 to 100	39 & above	H
9		14 to 14-5	101 to 105		
10	60 to 61	14-6 to 14-11	106 to 110		
11		15 to 15-5	111 to 115		
12	62 to 63	15-6 to 15-11	116 to 120		
13		16 to 16-5	121 to 125		
14	64 to 65	16-6 to 16-11	126 to 130		
15	66 to 67	17 to 17-5	131 to 133		
16	68	17-6 to 17-11	134 to 136		
17	69 & over	18 & over	137 & over		

Sample Achievement Scale
Running High Jump (Boys) - Height in Feet and Inches

T-Score	A	B	C	D	E	F	G	H	T-Score
50	3' 4"	3' 6"	--	--	--	4' 2"	--	--	50
49	--	--	3' 8"	3' 10"	4' 0"	--	4' 3"	--	49
48	--	--	--	--	--	--	--	4' 4"	48
47	3' 3"	--	--	--	--	--	--	--	47
46	--	3' 5"	3' 7"	3' 9"	3' 11"	4' 1"	4' 2"	--	46
45	--	--	--	--	--	--	--	4' 3"	45
44	3' 2"	--	--	--	--	--	--	--	44
43	--	3' 4"	--	--	3' 10"	4' 0"	--	--	43
42	--	--	3' 6"	3' 8"	--	--	4' 1"	--	42
41	3' 1"	--	--	--	--	--	--	4' 2"	41
40	--	3' 3"	--	--	3' 9"	3' 11"	--	--	40
39	--	--	3' 5"	3' 7"	--	--	4' 0"	--	39
38	3' 0"	--	--	--	--	--	--	4' 1"	38
37	--	3' 2"	--	--	--	3' 10"	--	--	37
36	--	--	3' 4"	3' 6"	3' 8"	--	3' 11"	--	36
35	2' 11"	--	--	--	--	--	--	4' 0"	35
34	--	3' 1"	--	--	--	3' 9"	--	--	34
33	--	--	3' 3"	3' 5"	3' 7"	--	3' 10"	--	33
32	--	--	--	--	--	--	--	3' 11"	32
31	2' 10"	3' 0"	--	--	--	3' 8"	--	--	31
30	--	--	3' 2"	3' 4"	3' 6"	--	3' 9"	--	30
29	--	--	--	--	--	--	--	3' 10"	29
28	2' 9"	--	--	--	--	--	--	--	28
27	--	2' 11"	3' 1"	3' 3"	3' 5"	3' 7"	3' 8"	--	27
26	--	--	--	--	--	--	--	3' 9"	26
25	2' 8"	--	--	--	--	--	--	--	25
24	--	2' 10"	--	--	3' 4"	3' 6"	--	--	24
23	--	--	3' 0"	3' 2"	--	--	3' 7"	--	23
22	2' 7"	--	--	--	--	--	--	3' 8"	22
21	--	2' 9"	--	--	3' 3"	3' 5"	--	--	21
20	--	--	2' 11"	3' 1"	--	--	3' 6"	--	20
19	2' 6"	--	--	--	--	--	--	3' 7"	19
18	--	2' 8"	--	--	--	3' 4"	--	--	18
17	--	--	2' 10"	3' 0"	3' 2"	--	3' 5"	--	17
16	2' 5"	--	--	--	--	--	--	3' 6"	16
15	--	2' 7"	--	--	--	3' 3"	--	--	15
14	--	--	2' 9"	2' 11"	3' 1"	--	3' 4"	--	14
13	--	--	--	--	--	--	--	3' 5"	13
12	2' 4"	2' 6"	--	--	--	3' 2"	--	--	12
11	--	--	2' 8"	2' 10"	3' 0"	--	3' 3"	--	11
10	--	--	--	--	--	--	--	3' 4"	10
9	2' 3"	--	--	--	--	--	--	--	9
8	--	2' 5"	2' 7"	2' 9"	2' 11"	3' 1"	3' 2"	--	8
7	--	--	--	--	--	--	--	3' 3"	7
6	2' 2"	--	--	--	--	--	--	--	6
5	--	2' 4"	--	--	2' 10"	3' 0"	--	--	5
4	--	--	2' 6"	2' 8"	--	--	3' 1"	--	4
3	2' 1"	--	--	--	--	--	--	3' 2"	3
2	--	2' 3"	--	--	2' 9"	2' 11"	--	--	2
1	--	--	2' 5"	2' 7"	--	--	3' 0"	--	1

Appendix   67

Sample Achievement Scale
Running High Jump (Boys) - Height in Feet and Inches

T-Score	A	B	C	D	E	F	G	H	T-Score
100	--	4' 10"	5' 0"	5' 2"	5' 4"	5' 6"	5' 7"	--	100
99	--	--	--	--	--	--	--	--	99
98	4' 7"	--	--	--	--	--	--	5' 8"	98
97	--	4' 9"	4' 11"	5' 1"	5' 3"	5' 5"	5' 6"	--	97
96	--	--	--	--	--	--	--	--	96
95	4' 6"	--	--	--	--	--	--	5' 7"	95
94	--	4' 8"	--	--	5' 2"	5' 4"	--	--	94
93	--	--	4' 10"	5' 0"	--	--	5' 5"	--	93
92	--	--	--	--	--	--	--	5' 6"	92
91	4' 5"	4' 7"	--	--	--	5' 3"	--	--	91
90	--	--	4' 9"	4' 11"	5' 1"	--	5' 4"	--	90
89	--	--	--	--	--	--	--	5' 5"	89
88	4' 4"	4' 6"	--	--	--	5' 2"	--	--	88
87	--	--	4' 8"	4' 10"	5' 0"	--	5' 3"	--	87
86	--	--	--	--	--	--	--	5' 4"	86
85	4' 3"	--	--	--	--	--	--	--	85
84	--	4' 5"	4' 7"	4' 9"	4' 11"	5' 1"	5' 2"	--	84
83	--	--	--	--	--	--	--	5' 3"	83
82	4' 2"	--	--	--	--	--	--	--	82
81	--	4' 4"	4' 6"	4' 8"	4' 10"	5' 0"	5' 1"	--	81
80	--	--	--	--	--	--	--	--	80
79	4' 1"	--	--	--	--	--	--	5' 2"	79
78	--	4' 3"	4' 5"	4' 7"	4' 9"	4' 11"	5' 0"	--	78
77	--	--	--	--	--	--	--	--	77
76	4' 0"	--	--	--	--	--	--	5' 1"	76
75	--	4' 2"	--	--	4' 8"	4' 10"	--	--	75
74	--	--	4' 4"	4' 6"	--	--	4' 11"	--	74
73	--	--	--	--	--	--	--	5' 0"	73
72	3' 11"	4' 1"	--	--	--	4' 9"	--	--	72
71	--	--	4' 3"	4' 5"	4' 7"	--	4' 10"	--	71
70	--	--	--	--	--	--	--	4' 11"	70
69	3' 10"	4' 0"	--	--	--	4' 8"	--	--	69
68	--	--	4' 2"	4' 4"	4' 6"	--	4' 9"	--	68
67	--	--	--	--	--	--	--	4' 10"	67
66	3' 9"	--	--	--	--	--	--	--	66
65	--	3' 11"	4' 1"	4' 3"	4' 5"	4' 7"	4' 8"	--	65
64	--	--	--	--	--	--	--	4' 9"	64
63	3' 8"	--	--	--	--	--	--	--	63
62	--	3' 10"	4' 0"	4' 2"	4' 4"	4' 6"	4' 7"	--	62
61	--	--	--	--	--	--	--	--	61
60	3' 7"	--	--	--	--	--	--	4' 8"	60
59	--	3' 9"	3' 11"	4' 1"	4' 3"	4' 5"	4' 6"	--	59
58	--	--	--	--	--	--	--	--	58
57	3' 6"	--	--	--	--	--	--	4' 7"	57
56	--	3' 8"	--	--	4' 2"	4' 4"	--	--	56
55	--	--	3' 10"	4' 0"	--	--	4' 5"	--	55
54	--	--	--	--	--	--	--	4' 6"	54
53	3' 5"	3' 7"	--	--	--	4' 3"	--	--	53
52	--	--	3' 9"	3' 11"	4' 1"	--	4' 4"	--	52
51	--	--	--	--	--	--	--	4' 5"	51

68   Statistics, Tests and Measurements in Physical Education

Classification Plan for Secondary School Boys[1]
Grades 7 to 12 inclusive

For purposes of competition in inter-school athletics and in individual events--derived from the formula 2A (years) + .475H (inches) + .16W (pounds)

Exponent	Age	Height	Weight	Exponent	Age	Height	Weight
9			53- 59	24	11:9-12:2	49½-51½	147-153
10			60- 65	25	12:3-12:8	52 -53½	154-159
11	Class	Sum of Expo.	66- 71	26	12:9-13:2	54 -55½	160-165
12			72- 78	27	13:3-13:8	56 -57½	166-171
13	F	69 and below	79- 84	28	13:9-14:2	58 -59½	172-178
14	E	70-74	85- 90	29	14:3-14:8	60 -62	179-184
15	D	75-78	91- 96	30	14:9-15:2	62½-64	185-190
16	C	79-82	97-103	31	15:3-15:8	64½-66	191- up
17	B	83-87	104-109	32	15:9-16:2	66½-68	
18	A	88 and over	110-115	33	16:3-16:8	68½-70½	
19			116-121	34	16:9-17:2	71 -72½	
20			122-128	35	17:3-17:8	73 -74½	
21			129-134	36	17:9-18:2	75 -up	
22	10:9-11:2	47 down	135-140	37	18:3-18:8		
23	11:3-11:8	47½-49	141-146	38	18:9-19:2		

Note: Height is measured in half-inches. The boy must have attained the height listed before the exponent value changes. For example, he remains at 49 until he reaches 49½.

[1] Adopted by the California Interscholastic Federation at its annual meeting, May 1935.

Chart for Height-Weight Class Division of College Men

	Height	Slender	Medium	Heavy
			Weight	
Short	4-11	up to 92	93-108	109 up
	5-0	up to 97	98-112	113 up
	5-1	up to 101	102-117	118 up
	5-2	up to 106	107-121	122 up
	5-3	up to 110	111-126	127 up
	5-4	up to 114	115-131	132 up
	5-5	up to 118	119-135	136 up
	5-6	up to 121	122-139	140 up
Medium	5-7	up to 124	125-143	144 up
	5-8	up to 128	129-147	148 up
	5-9	up to 131	132-150	151 up
	5-10	up to 134	135-153	154 up
Tall	5-11	up to 138	139-157	158 up
	6-0	up to 142	143-162	163 up
	6-1	up to 146	147-166	167 up
	6-2	up to 150	151-171	172 up
	6-3	up to 154	155-175	176 up
	6-4	up to 158	159-179	180 up